THE

'Excuse me,' Lilicat said, 'but we're looking for a Vanessa Grant.'

The man looked up at them with a sharp gaze. 'She isn't part of this flea market.'

'But she was,' McKenzie insisted. 'She told us she used to work in the theater as a wardrobe mistress,' she added. 'Lilith just bought a gypsy costume from her.'

The man rocked back on his heels. 'Well, you're right about that. She did do a stint in the theater, quite some years ago.'

'Then you know her,' McKenzie pressed.

'*Knew* her,' the man answered. 'Vanessa Grant died in a fire three years ago.'

TITLES IN THE POWER SERIES
by JESSE HARRIS

THE POWER

THE
POSSESSION

by Jesse Harris

RED FOX

A Red Fox Book

Published by Random House Children's Books
20 Vauxhall Bridge Road, London SW1V 2SA

A division of Random House UK Ltd.

London Melbourne Sydney Auckland Johannesburg
and agencies throughout the world

First published in the United States by
Alfred A. Knopf, Inc. 1992

Red Fox edition 1993

Phototypeset by Intype, London
Printed and bound in Great Britain by
Cox & Wyman Ltd, Reading, Berkshire

ISBN 0 09 922091 1

CHAPTER 1

'**I have got** to have this!' exclaimed Lilith Caine, holding up a small, flowered metallic pig.

McKenzie Gold smiled at her friend's enthusiasm. 'Put it down, Lilicat,' she advised. 'You do *not* need a piggy bank that speaks French.'

'But it's so cute,' Lilicat said. She put a penny in the slot in the middle of the pig's back. The pig made a vaguely French sound. 'See, it says *merci*. It's really incredibly polite.'

McKenzie rolled her gray-green eyes and walked on toward the next booth at the outdoor flea market. Lilicat caught up with her a few minutes later. 'Did you buy it?' McKenzie asked.

'Not yet, but I'm thinking about it.'

'You know, there *is* something we might find

here,' McKenzie said, flipping through an old photo album.

Lilicat giggled and pointed to a sepia-tinted photograph of an old woman with big buck teeth. 'That looks just like my great-aunt Olga.'

'Seriously,' McKenzie went on, 'we have to find costumes for Erin Livingston's party.'

Lilicat groaned. 'Why did Erin Livingston have to be born on October eighteenth?' she asked. 'I mean, if you're going to have an annual Halloween-birthday party, you really ought to have the decency to be born at the end of the month. Every single year we have to put our costumes together two whole weeks before anyone actually celebrates Halloween.' She looked around at the oak and maple trees, whose leaves were just starting to turn. 'It's only the first weekend in October. It's too early to deal with all this stuff.'

McKenzie, who had heard these complaints since the fourth grade when Erin Livingston had transferred into their class, said nothing. She knew Lilicat would get over it when she found the right costume.

Lilicat wandered over to a table filled with antique jewelry, picked up a silver and turquoise necklace, and draped it around her forehead. 'Cleopatra,' she said, batting her eyelashes.

McKenzie studied her friend. With her big brown eyes, bangs, and straight, dark hair that fell just above her shoulders, she might actually pass for Cleopatra – a short Cleopatra. In her stocking feet, Lilicat was barely five foot two, and hated to be reminded of it. 'Close,' McKenzie said tactfully, 'except Cleopatra probably didn't wear Native American jewelry.'

'Details, mere details,' Lilicat said airily, putting the necklace down and going on to the next stand, which featured a collection of old hurricane lamps.

McKenzie scanned the array of tables. Whether or not they found anything for Erin's party, it was a perfect fall day to be wandering around an outdoor flea market. Most of what was for sale was pure junk, but the air was crisp and clear, and somehow everything looked intriguing if not appealing.

A cool wind blew through the trees, and McKenzie hugged her sweater tight around her. Actually, it wasn't her sweater. It belonged to her boyfriend, Aidan. As far as McKenzie was concerned, there was no chance he'd ever get it back. The dark green wool was perfect against her fair, freckled skin and her long, straight auburn hair. Besides, the oversize sweater was warm and cozy and it reminded her of him.

She caught sight of Lilicat examining an old manual typewriter. She smiled. Lilicat was such a pushover for anything 'antique'. If I don't stop her, McKenzie thought, she'll probably buy that rickety old thing. And she can barely type! She saw just the distraction she needed – a stall filled with old clothing.

'Lilicat,' she said, taking Lilicat by the elbow and steering her gently in the direction of the stall, 'take a look at this.'

Lilicat gave her a mock glare but allowed herself to be led.

The stall turned out to be even better than McKenzie had hoped. Deep wooden steamer trunks overflowed with silks and satins and laces. A clothing rack stood beneath two trees, bent with the weight of brocade robes and taffeta gowns. And on a cast-iron hatrack were hats of every description – straw bonnets and derbies, cowboy hats and sombreros, leopard-print pillbox hats and even a turban set with a great fake sapphire. Then McKenzie felt a momentary chill streak through her; she pulled her sweater tighter.

'Good afternoon,' said a red-haired woman, emerging from behind an oval mirror. 'What can I do for you on such a lovely day? I've got dresses, jackets, scarves . . .' McKenzie felt herself staring. She couldn't help it. The woman was extra-ordinary looking. Long red hair cascaded wildly down over her blouse, which was sewn of emer-ald and purple silk. Beneath this she wore an ankle-length brocade skirt that might have been black and might have been midnight blue. McKenzie couldn't tell. Whatever it was, it had a strange, dark sheen.

Lilicat seemed hypnotized by the woman's appearance. 'I love your jewelry,' she said in an awestruck voice. 'It's outrageous.'

Too outrageous, McKenzie thought. She said nothing, but her eyes lingered on the countless gold bangles, the necklaces strung with silver and glass beads, the rings flashing cut stones of every color, and the two crystal earrings in the woman's left ear that seemed green one minute, lavender the next.

The woman's heavily made-up eyes came to rest on Lilicat. 'And I was admiring your jacket,' the woman said.

'This?' Lilicat examined her studded denim jacket with surprise. She looked at McKenzie as if to say, 'Am I missing something here?' McKenzie had been with her when she bought the jacket in the Lakeville Mall. It was hardly unique – there had been at least twenty others on the rack, and Lilicat had almost decided not to buy it because she was sure everyone in Lakeville High would have one like it.

The woman ran a finger lightly over the studs on Lilicat's left wrist. 'You've got a very fine eye for clothing.' She gave her a dazzling smile. 'And I've got very good prices today.' She pulled a cotton eyelet petticoat from the rack. 'All the girls are wearing these now. Put a little jacket on top of it and you'll have an outfit straight out of a fashion magazine.'

Lilicat shook her head. 'Actually, we're looking for Halloween costumes. Do you have something . . . I don't know . . . something sort of Egyptian?'

'I think I have just the thing.' The woman began to dig through one of the trunks, pulling out colorful scarves, gloves, blouses, vests, nightgowns, and kimonos. McKenzie felt as if she were watching a magician pull things out of a hat.

'Ooooh!' Lilicat said softly as a black silk shawl floated to the ground. The shawl was embroidered with brilliantly colored flowers and leaves. 'This is gorgeous!'

The woman turned around. 'Now, that's a find,' she said approvingly. 'Wear that shawl and the man of your dreams will fall in love with you.'

'Oh, right,' Lilicat said, giggling.

The woman's eyes slid over her again, measuring her up and down. 'There must be someone,' she said slowly. 'Some boy you've secretly longed for. I can see him now. He's very good looking, and you've known him for a while now. You think about him all the time. You just never believe he might be thinking about you.'

McKenzie scowled as Lilicat's eyes went wide. But she had to admit, this woman sounded convincing. Either she was a great con artist or she really believed what she was saying. 'Wear the shawl, and he'll notice you,' she went on. 'First he'll notice you, then he won't be able to get you out of his mind. Before you know it, you'll have the romance you've always wanted.' She draped the shawl around Lilicat's shoulders and turned her so that she faced the mirror. 'It looks beautiful on you, and it'll bring you the man of your dreams. Can you really afford to pass it up?'

'It's not exactly Egyptian,' McKenzie pointed out.

'No,' the woman agreed. 'But I have something . . . a skirt, I think . . . from a production of *Antony and Cleopatra*.' She winked at McKenzie. 'Once upon a time, many years ago, I worked in the theater.' She dipped into a graceful curtsy. 'Vanessa Grant, wardrobe mistress, at your service.'

That explains her theatrical manner, McKenzie thought, and yet something still didn't feel right. She wondered briefly how long ago 'once upon a time' was. It was impossible to guess the woman's age. She could have been anywhere from twenty-five to fifty-five.

'Maybe I don't want to be Cleopatra,' Lilicat said, thoughtfully examining her reflection. She took a long, green satin skirt from the rack and held it against her waist. 'Maybe I should go to Erin's party as a gypsy fortuneteller . . .'

McKenzie felt the chill race through her again, and this time she knew it wasn't the crisp fall air. It was the special sense she'd had since childhood, and it was warning her about something. McKenzie didn't really know what to call this ability of hers. The word 'psychic' sounded so hokey. It wasn't as if she could bend forks or channel spirits. All she knew was that from the time she was a little girl she'd had these dreams and visions and certain – instincts – about things.

When she was very young, she'd had so many dreams while awake that her parents had taken her to a psychologist to be tested. The tests hadn't proved anything. But McKenzie had continued to dream of events before they happened, to sense certain people's intentions, and to feel things that had no logical explanation. Over the years she had learned to trust this ability, and now it was warning her away from the stall. She was sure of it.

'Lilicat,' she said quickly, 'why don't you hold off on deciding on a costume until after we've looked at some of the other booths?' She gave Vanessa Grant a quick, forced smile. 'Thanks for showing us your stuff. Maybe we'll be back later.'

The woman raised one penciled eyebrow. 'Whatever you like.'

McKenzie grabbed Lilicat by the elbow and tugged her away from the antique clothing stall.

'I wasn't ready to leave,' Lilicat protested, shaking her arm free. 'I wanted to buy that shawl. It looked great.'

'It did look great,' McKenzie said, feeling slightly embarrassed. 'I'm sorry I pulled you away, but I was getting chills back there.'

Lilicat rolled her eyes. 'I told you to wear a jacket. Do you want to borrow mine? After all,' she teased, 'I've got a very fine eye for clothing.'

McKenzie groaned. 'I don't want to borrow your jacket. It wasn't that kind of chill. It was . . . that feeling I get sometimes. It was trying to warn me of something.'

'Look, Mack,' Lilicat said patiently, 'I know this psychic thing of yours is legit. You've definitely got some telepathic something or other working for you. But you've also got Aidan Collins – the perfect, gorgeous boyfriend.'

'What's that got to do with anything?'

'Do you know how long it's been since the last time I went out with a boy? Do you remember what it's like to go to every school dance with a group of your girlfriends?'

McKenzie winced in sympathy. Although Lilicat had always been popular, she'd had a run of bad luck lately. Guys asked her out all the time, but they all seemed to be either dumb jocks or dweeb city.

'Listen, Mack,' Lilicat went on, 'the woman said that if I wear that shawl, the man of my dreams will fall in love with me, and – '

'And you really believe that?'

'At this point, I'm willing to try anything. I'm buying it.'

Lilicat turned and headed back toward Vanessa Grant's booth. McKenzie had no choice but to follow. When she caught up with her, McKenzie found her already draped in the silk shawl and admiring herself in the mirror.

'Now, isn't that pretty?' Vanessa Grant cooed.

Even McKenzie had to admit the shawl looked beautiful on Lilicat, but the feverish chill was back, and she was beginning to feel a growing sense of dread.

The woman held up the satin skirt that Lilicat had looked at earlier. 'You've got a good eye for color,' she observed. 'The skirt brings out the greens in the shawl.'

Lilicat flushed at the compliment. 'Don't you think it would make a perfect gypsy costume?' she asked McKenzie. She picked up a gold-and-green-patterned blouse from the top of another trunk.

There must be some way I can get her away from this booth, McKenzie told herself. 'That's a terrific gypsy costume,' she agreed.

'I'll give you the whole thing for seventeen dollars,' Vanessa Grant offered.

'Sold,' said Lilicat happily. They concluded the deal quickly, and Vanessa put her purchases in a brown paper bag.

'Remember,' she called out as the girls left her booth, 'the man of your dreams.'

'And a million dollars,' McKenzie mumbled sarcastically.

'The man of my dreams will do just fine,' Lilicat told her, grinning.

As the girls moved farther from Vanessa Grant's stall, McKenzie began to relax. Whatever her special sense had been trying to warn her about, she and Lilicat were well away from it now. They wandered into a few other booths, stopping at one to try on oversize men's coats. 'Funky but ridiculous,' McKenzie pronounced, studying her reflection.

'Agreed.' Lilicat stripped off the coat she'd tried on and began checking out a rack of dresses.

'Now what?' McKenzie asked. 'I thought you just bought a costume.'

'I'm not looking for me,' Lilicat replied. 'I'm looking for you – and I think I've got just the thing. Close your eyes.'

McKenzie shut her eyes. She was afraid to open them again. Last year Lilicat had been convinced that McKenzie should dress up as Pippi Longstocking. ('Your freckles are perfect!' her friend had insisted. 'It's an absolute waste if you aren't Pippi!') She didn't even want to see what Lilicat had in mind now.

'Open your eyes, Mack,' Lilicat said. 'You're going to like this one. I promise.'

McKenzie opened one eye and then the other and was surprised to see that she did indeed like what Lilicat had chosen. It was a short, pale ivory shift with a long fringe around the top – a perfect flapper's costume.

'Can you shimmy?' Lilicat asked.

'Not exactly.'

'How about the Charleston?'

McKenzie just stared at her friend.

'Don't worry.' Lilicat nudged her toward the man who ran the booth. 'Pay the man for the dress and I'll teach you.'

As the two girls returned to the car, they had a heated discussion about whether or not Lilicat could teach McKenzie to dance like a flapper. 'Forget it,' said McKenzie. 'You're a cheerleader. You're one of the most coordinated people in the entire school. I, on the other hand – '

'The Charleston isn't that complicated,' Lilicat insisted.

McKenzie opened the trunk of her parents' Toyota, and they tossed their purchases inside. 'I appreciate the offer,' she said with a grin, 'but every time you've tried to teach me to dance or throw a ball or do anything remotely athletic, it's been a total disaster.'

'Not true. I taught you to play a very hot game of checkers.'

McKenzie groaned and got into the car. 'We'll talk about it later,' she promised.

They drove home, cruising along the winding

13

rural roads that lay on the outskirts of Lakeville. Sometimes the town could be so pretty. Like right now. The late afternoon sun was making the fields look almost golden. It all seemed so peaceful, McKenzie almost forgot about the feelings of danger she'd had a few minutes before.

Almost.

Half an hour later she pulled up in front of Lilicat's house and popped open the trunk.

'I'll call you tomorrow,' Lilicat promised, getting out of the car.

McKenzie heard the trunk slam shut and then saw Lilicat walking up her drive, the paper bag containing the gypsy costume in her left hand. She put the Toyota in gear and was ready to pull out when she heard Lilicat shout her name. For some reason, it scared her.

'I took the wrong bag,' Lilicat called to her from her front door.

'I'll get it,' McKenzie called back. She parked the car again, got out, and opened the trunk. There was the other brown paper bag. She reached for it. Instantly she drew back her hand with a cry of pain. Her palm was burning.

CHAPTER 2

McKenzie **was only** half awake when she walked through the doors of Lakeville High on Monday morning. She hadn't slept well the night before. To say the least. Why had the paper bag burned her hand? The question had kept her tossing and turning all night. Now she hung her jacket in her locker, sorted through the books that were sliding off the top shelf, and scanned the crowded hallway, looking for Lilicat. Seeing no sign of her friend, she shrugged and headed for homeroom.

Michael 'Lumpy' Johnson, the sports editor of the school paper, the *Guardian*, was walking toward her, a concerned expression on his face. Oh no, she thought, not again.

Lumpy came to a stop directly in front of her,

deliberately blocking her way. 'Hey, Gold. You finish your column yet?'

'Michael,' McKenzie said patiently, 'it's rude to nag someone about their column before nine in the morning. I'm still half asleep. Besides, you're sports – what do you care about my features column?'

Michael, who stood nearly six feet three, patted her on the head. 'Just want to make sure all the *Guardian* editors are doing their jobs.'

Even though she and Lumpy were headed for the same homeroom, McKenzie turned around and walked in the opposite direction. Lumpy Johnson meant well, but she couldn't deal with him until second period at least.

She walked directly into a tall, good-looking senior with longish, shaggy blond hair. 'Morning, Mack,' said Aidan, giving her a quick kiss.

'Thank goodness it's you,' she said. 'I just started my morning with a progress check from Lumpy Johnson.'

'Tell me about it,' said Aidan with a sigh. As a photographer for the *Guardian*, he took most of the school's sports photos. 'Johnson called me three different times this weekend to see if I had shots from Wednesday's football game. I think he wanted me to hand-deliver them to his house or something.'

'He takes his job very seriously,' McKenzie agreed, grinning. Somehow talking to Aidan made things funny instead of annoying. 'Have you seen Lilicat today?'

'Nope.' The first bell rang. 'But I got a dynamite picture of her at the last game.'

'She'll love you,' McKenzie promised.

'Aren't we supposed to be in our homerooms?' Aidan asked, idly playing with a strand of McKenzie's hair.

'Yeah, but . . . I've got a brilliant idea – let's trade homerooms.'

'Oh no,' Aidan said, backing away. 'I refuse to start my day with Lumpy Johnson. See you at lunch, okay?'

'After sticking me with Lumpy?' McKenzie joked. But Aidan was already down the hall. Feeling better, McKenzie headed for her own homeroom.

She finally caught up with Lilicat at lunch. She found her and Erin Livingston in the cafeteria, sitting at a table over by the windows. Lilicat had already discarded the orange-colored stuff on her plate and was using her fork to push at something the school called bread-pudding. 'It's resilient,' she announced. 'It even bounces.'

McKenzie set her tray down beside her best friend. 'What did you expect?'

Lilicat poked at the pudding again. 'This is great,' she said. 'If we ever run out of rubber plants, we've got a natural substitute right here at Lakeville. I mean, the school could make a fortune off this stuff.'

'If it doesn't poison us first,' Erin agreed. She pushed her dessert plate aside and smiled at McKenzie. 'Lilicat says she's coming to my party as a gypsy. What are you going to be?'

'A flapper,' McKenzie answered.

'That is if I can teach her to flap,' Lilicat put in. 'She needs some work on the Charleston.'

'How's this?' asked McKenzie, flapping her elbow into Lilicat's ribs. Aidan chose that moment to join them. 'Glad to see you two getting along, as usual,' he said cheerfully. 'Hi, Erin.'

'Hey, Aidan. Do you know what you're going to be for my party?'

'Mmmm,' mumbled Aidan with his mouth full.

He had already attacked his sandwich and eaten several bites. McKenzie could never figure out how Aidan ate the cafeteria food with so much pleasure. Deep down she suspected he had lost his taste buds years ago and never even knew it. 'Well,' he said at last, 'Mack is going as a flapper, so I've been thinking about being a twenties gangster.'

McKenzie raised her eyebrows in surprise. This was the first she'd heard of his plan.

'I'll teach you to dance too,' Lilicat immediately offered.

Aidan cleared his throat. 'Thanks, but I think I'd better see if I can find a violin case first.'

'Coward,' McKenzie teased.

Aidan grinned. 'You'd better be careful what you say to a gangster, girl.'

'Or to a Lakeville *cheer*leader,' Lilicat added, with mock self-importance. It was one of the things McKenzie liked best about her friend. Although Lilicat loved cheering, she'd always thought it ridiculous that everyone acted as if cheerleaders were automatically the coolest people on earth.

Aidan reached for his notebook and pulled out a flat brown envelope. 'Take a look at these, Miss Cheerleader.'

Lilicat opened the envelope and took out three eight-by-ten black-and-white glossies. The first showed Lilicat in a jump, her legs in an almost perfect split.

'God, Lilicat,' Erin said, 'you're about a foot higher off the ground than everyone else.'

The second picture was of a smiling Lilicat

doing a pompom routine, but it was the third photograph that McKenzie couldn't stop looking at. Aidan had caught Lilicat in a moment between routines, when she'd stood watching the game beside the stadium fence, her head resting on her arms. It was a quiet, dreamy pose, and Lilicat looked absolutely gorgeous. McKenzie felt as if Aidan had noticed a part of Lilicat that not many people knew. He'd seen the very best part of her friend and somehow captured it on film. It made McKenzie happy, and it also made her feel a little strange. Strange? Let's face it, she told herself, I may be a tiny bit envious. Aidan had never taken a picture like that of her.

'These are incredible, Aidan,' Erin said.

'They really are,' McKenzie agreed, pushing aside her jealous feelings. 'Lilicat, you look beautiful – especially in this dreamy one here.'

Lilicat was blushing.

'They're for you, if you want them,' Aidan offered, pushing the photos toward her. 'I've got other prints.'

Lilicat smiled at him. 'Thanks, Aidan.'

McKenzie looked up and saw Lumpy Johnson coming toward their table. 'Oh no,' she muttered, 'I think Lumpy is about to strike again.'

Aidan smiled at her. 'Don't you and I have to

pick up a book from the library? You know, that really important book?'

McKenzie smiled back at him. 'Definitely.'

They left the cafeteria arm in arm.

On Thursday McKenzie left history class late. They'd just had an essay test and, as usual, McKenzie wound up writing more than necessary. It was a bad habit. Once she got started writing anything, it was hard for her to stop. Minutes after the bell rang, McKenzie was still at her desk, working on the final question. She'd finished up only when the next class had come in and her teacher had insisted that she hand in the blue book.

What am I trying to do? Write an encyclopedia? she berated herself as she walked down the hall. How will I ever get through college if I keep this up? She pictured the rest of the college emptying out after finals. Summer would come and the whole campus would be empty – except for McKenzie Gold, who'd still be sitting in some stuffy lecture hall, finishing essay questions on the final exam.

The sight of Aidan at the end of the hallway took her mind off essay questions. His back was to her, but she'd know him anywhere. There was no way she could mistake his tall, lean frame or the faded jeans he wore nearly every day. He was talking to Lilicat, who was wearing the silk shawl she'd bought at the flea market. *Why in the world is Lilicat wearing her Halloween costume?* McKenzie wondered. *Now everyone will see it before the party.*

McKenzie watched as Lilicat put her hand on Aidan's shoulder. The gesture was casual – so easy and casual it made McKenzie come to an abrupt halt. The way Lilicat touched Aidan was the way a girl touches a boy she knows very well.

McKenzie stood for a moment, feeling a mixture of embarrassment and confusion. *Did I just see what I think I saw?* she asked herself. *Is Lilicat flirting with Aidan?*

Of course not, she answered herself at once. *Lilicat would never do something like that. She *was* standing awfully close, but after all, they're good friends, and since when is standing close to someone a criminal offense? I'm becoming totally paranoid!*

Shaking off the thought, McKenzie started walking toward them again. And that's when she saw it. She blinked, once again doubting her own eyes. *What is that stuff on Aidan's shirt? It's staining the shirt red!* McKenzie felt herself stiffen with horror. *No. It can't be . . .*

But it was. Blood was oozing from the place where Lilicat's hand rested on Aidan's shoulder. His white shirt was covered in dark red blood.

CHAPTER 3

Blood was everywhere. McKenzie watched in disbelief as it flowed over Aidan's clothes. Aidan reached up and touched the spot on his shoulder where the blood was coming from. Obviously puzzled by what he felt, he brought his hand back down, looked at it in amazement, then jumped back from Lilicat. McKenzie saw his face go white with horror.

'Aidan!' McKenzie screamed, and ran toward them through the empty hall.

Time seemed to slow to a halt. Aidan turned and looked at her in confusion. He seemed such a long distance away.

Let me get to him in time, McKenzie prayed as she raced toward him.

'Mack!' Aidan's voice was alarmed.

McKenzie pushed herself, running full out.

Finally she was at his side. She reached for him, trying to stop the flow of blood.

Aidan pulled away from her. 'Don't touch me. You'll get it all over you. It's already all over me and Lilicat.'

'Never mind that,' McKenzie said frantically, reaching for him again. 'You're hurt.'

'Hurt?'

'Your back!'

Aidan glanced over his shoulder. 'My back is fine. Wet, but fine.'

His words filtered through her panic, and McKenzie saw that his back *was* fine. There was no wound. No blood. The 'blood' was not blood at all but rusty water.

McKenzie looked at Aidan again and then quickly up at the ceiling. A pipe had cracked and was leaking rusty water through the white ceiling tiles. 'Oh, God,' she stammered, 'it – it's leaking.'

'No kidding,' Lilicat said, gingerly stepping around the puddle on the floor.

McKenzie wasn't just breathing hard; she was trembling. 'How about you?' Aidan asked her. 'Are you okay?'

She flushed with embarrassment. She didn't feel like admitting that she thought she had seen blood flowing down his shirt. And there was no way she was going to admit that Lilicat putting her hand on Aidan's shoulder had made her jealous. Besides, she wondered, was it really jealousy? *Am I really that possessive? How could I mistrust the two people I'm closest to?* She shook her head. It all seemed so silly now.

'Uh . . . I thought the two of you were in danger,' McKenzie said lamely. 'I thought you might drown in a puddle or something.' She tried to turn it into a joke and laugh, but it didn't work. Both of her friends looked at her as if she were losing it.

Aidan gave his shirt an irritated glance. 'I'd better go,' he said. 'I'm late for trig. Catch you two later.'

'We're all late,' McKenzie said. 'What do you have next, Lilicat – French? I'm going that way too. I'll walk you.'

Lilicat held up one end of the silk shawl where the print was darkened by a circle of rust. 'Look at this,' she said with a moan. 'I've got rusty water all over my new shawl. I've got to wash it off before the stain sets.'

'Wash it after French,' McKenzie advised. 'You know Madame LaRue's been on the warpath about kids coming late.'

Acting as if she hadn't heard her, Lilicat

turned in the opposite direction and started toward the girls' room.

McKenzie stared after her. It wasn't like Lilicat to ignore her. Or to be so unconcerned about making a teacher mad. McKenzie hurried after her. 'I'll come with you,' she offered.

Lilicat glanced at her and shrugged. 'Up to you.'

They were about as far from the girls' room as they could possibly be. It was around the corner, way down at the end of the other hallway. McKenzie was conscious of how empty the halls were. Lilicat wasn't the only one who'd wind up with detention.

'Hey, Lilicat.' Chris Andreas, the first-string quarterback who'd taken over when Bob Kowalski broke his wrist, walked toward them, books under his arm. 'You're lookin' good today!'

'Hey, Andreas,' Lilicat shot back, 'you're looking . . . presentable.'

Chris grinned and swaggered toward them. He'd won every game he'd played, bringing Lakeville to the top of their division, and he moved with the cocky strut of a jock who knows he's the best. 'Presentable?' he echoed. He shook his thick blond hair out of his eyes. 'You're talking to the hottest dude in Lakeville, and all you can come up with is *presentable*?'

27

Lilicat smiled up at him, adjusting the shawl so that it slid off her shoulders. 'I guess you'll do,' she said softly.

McKenzie couldn't believe what she was hearing. Chris Andreas was definitely hot looking and pretty exciting to watch on a football field. But he had a long history of asking girls out and dumping them two weeks later. Lilicat had sworn up and down that she'd never give him the time of day. And now here she was flirting with him!

'Andreas, you turkey.' Mark McConnel, the wide receiver, joined them, his eyes fixed on Lilicat. 'What are you doing with our sweet little cheerleader?'

Lilicat hooked her arm through Mark's. 'He was just telling me how modest and charming he is.'

This was getting more and more bizarre. McKenzie knew for a fact that Lilicat liked Mark even less than she liked Chris. 'Lilicat,' she said, 'we'd better get to class.'

Chris looked at her for the first time and winked. 'Didn't anyone tell you?' he joked. 'Football players don't have to go to class. All we have to do is walk around and look cool.'

Mark didn't pretend to be amused. 'What's

with you, Gold?' he demanded. 'If you're so afraid of being late, just go to class!'

McKenzie felt her face redden. 'Lilicat – ' she began, wanting her friend to get her out of this somehow.

Lilicat didn't even look at her. 'I've got to wash off my shawl,' she told the boys. 'Watch out for the ceilings here. This school is falling apart.' She ambled off toward the girls' room, leaving the two football players looking after her with a gleam in their eyes.

Wondering which one of them was going crazy, McKenzie trailed her friend to the restroom. Inside she found Lilicat standing in front of the sink, scrubbing at the shawl.

'Lilicat,' McKenzie asked tentatively. 'Are you all right?'

'Fine.'

'Are you sure?'

Lilicat looked up from the shawl. 'Why wouldn't I be?'

'I don't know,' McKenzie admitted. 'It's just . . . I didn't think you liked Chris or Mark.' An alarming thought went through her mind. What if either Chris or Mark was the man of Lilicat's dreams? Not that she believed that stuff, but she sure hoped it wasn't Mark. He had a mean streak that came out when you least expected it.

'They're all right,' Lilicat replied in a bored tone. Her concentration was back on the shawl.

McKenzie watched her friend with a sense of growing confusion. That didn't sound like Lilicat at all. Usually, Lilicat would give her an earful on the subject of jocks, and Chris and Mark in particular. But the only thing that seemed to interest her now was that crazy silk shawl.

'Is the stain really bad?' McKenzie asked, trying to get her talking.

Lilicat didn't answer.

'Here, let me help.' McKenzie soaked a paper towel in water and took an edge of the shawl.

Lilicat turned, her brown eyes furious. 'I can do that myself!' she snarled, snatching the cloth from McKenzie's hand.

For a moment McKenzie was stunned, unable to react. Lilicat – her best friend since kindergarten – was treating her like a stranger. She tried one last time. 'Lilicat?'

Lilicat took a deep breath, as if to calm herself. 'I'm sorry,' she said. 'It's just that it's old silk, and it's delicate, and I don't want anyone to touch it. Okay?'

'Okay,' McKenzie said. But she was still hurt.

'I'm going to class now,' she said. She left the restroom as quickly as she could.

CHAPTER 4

McKenzie studied herself in the full-length mirror on her bedroom door. Hmm . . . not bad. The ivory flapper dress just grazed her knees. The long strand of fake pearls she'd borrowed from her mother looked perfect with it. So did her headband, complete with its sequins and fluffy white feather. Lilicat had helped her with that.

Lilicat . . . McKenzie still hadn't made sense of that weird, awful Thursday when she'd seen the blood on Aidan's shirt, and Lilicat had acted so strange. She kept thinking about it. What did it mean?

Lilicat had been perfectly normal since then. McKenzie was glad she hadn't pushed her for an explanation. Lilicat had even come through with dance lessons, and much to her own amazement, McKenzie could now do a respectable Charleston.

'Mack . . .' her mother's voice floated up the stairs. 'Aidan's here for you.'

McKenzie gave herself one last glance in the mirror. If her hair were chin length instead of down past her shoulders, the look would be complete. No way, she thought, I'm not cutting my hair for a costume.

She did a few quick Charleston steps at the top of the landing and headed down the stairs, ready to greet her gangster.

Aidan was sitting on the corduroy living room sofa, talking with her father. The sight of him brought her up short.

He was not wearing a gangster suit and spats and carrying a violin case. Aidan was dressed all in black. Tight black jeans tucked into high black riding boots. A loose black shirt open at the throat, black gloves and cape, and a black mask concealing his eyes. If he hadn't been sitting in the living room asking her father about his metal sculptures, there would have been something genuinely sinister about him.

'I thought I was going to Erin's party with a gangster,' McKenzie said.

Aidan stood up and she saw that he wore a

sword at his side. 'Will a highwayman do, my lady?' he asked in a mock British accent.

Even though he looked outrageously handsome, something about the costume made McKenzie uneasy. 'I guess it will have to,' she answered.

'Oh, come on, Mack,' Aidan said, sounding very much like Aidan. 'You're not ticked off because our costumes don't match?'

'Of course not. I just wasn't expecting a highwayman.'

Aidan gave her a kiss on the cheek, the only sort he ever gave her when her parents were around. 'The night is full of surprises,' he whispered. 'And you look terrific. Let's get out of here.'

'This is all wrong,' Aidan said as he and McKenzie started up Erin's walk.

'What is?'

'The image. If I were doing this right, I'd be galloping up to the door on a midnight-black stallion.'

McKenzie remembered vividly when Aidan's obsession had been animals and becoming a vet. That was before his obsessions with tennis, astronomy, and photography. Aidan's hobbies seemed to change from one month to the next.

But while he was interested in something, he took it *very* seriously. McKenzie grinned. 'Don't tell me you're taking up riding?'

'Cruel lady, to joke about such a thing,' he said, returning to the British accent. 'I'll take a kiss from you for that.'

McKenzie wrinkled her nose. 'I don't know about kissing guys in masks. It's kind of creepy. And that dumb accent – '

'Oh, shut up,' Aidan murmured, pulling her toward him.

Still pretending to be reluctant, McKenzie tried to walk in the opposite direction. But when Aidan finally drew her near, it was she who kissed him first, lightly brushing her lips over his and then deepening the kiss, wanting him to know how completely crazy about him she was, how she'd never wanted anyone the way she wanted him. Aidan's hands were warm along her back, caressing her, pressing her close against him, making her think she was about to lose her mind.

'All right, all right,' said a good-natured voice. 'We all know you love each other. You can break it up now.'

McKenzie and Aidan broke apart quickly to see Chris Andreas coming up the walk with two other guys from the football team behind him.

Draped in white, they were dressed as . . . McKenzie wasn't sure what . . . ghosts? Mountains? Giant marshmallows? They all looked big and white and lumpy.

McKenzie straightened her headband, glad it was dark out, so no one could see how much she was blushing. Aidan still had one hand resting lightly on the back of her neck. It was going to take a while for her breathing to return to normal.

Unembarrassed, Chris and his friends strode past them and onto the porch. 'Trick or treat,' he called cheerfully.

Aidan ran a hand through McKenzie's hair. 'Do you want to go in?' he asked, his voice husky. 'We could go back to the car instead, maybe go for a ride and – '

'Welcome to the madness!' Erin Livingston, dressed as some kind of demented creature with lots of antennae sticking out of her head, threw open the door. 'Come on in, guys. And who's that still down on the walk – Mack and Aidan? Get in here, you two. Everyone's been asking for you.'

McKenzie and Aidan gave each other reluctant looks. 'Guess we should go in,' Aidan said softly.

McKenzie nodded and took his hand. Together they entered the house.

Erin's living room was wall-to-wall people. Two jack-o'-lanterns on the fireplace mantel cast eerie shadows along the walls. Except for the flickering blue readout on the CD player, the lanterns were the only lights in the room. McKenzie helped herself to a glass of punch and stood quietly, letting her eyes adjust to the dark. Ghouls, witches, monsters, Ninjas, and at least three Bart Simpsons danced to a hard-rock beat. She recognized most of the kids by the way they moved, though there were a few she couldn't be sure of.

'Check it out!' Aidan was by her side, nodding toward Lilicat. 'That's got to be the best costume here.'

Lilicat had crimped her normally straight black hair so that it curled in dark, wild waves above her shoulders. She wore the skirt and blouse and shawl that she'd bought from Vanessa Grant, and tons of jewelry. Her face was painted with heavy, dramatic makeup that made her eyes seem enormous. But it wasn't just the costume that was so impressive. Lilicat was whirling to the music, with her skirt and shawl flying.

McKenzie watched, fascinated. If she hadn't

known Lilicat since kindergarten, she might not have recognized her. This gypsy didn't move the way Lilicat moved. Her gestures were more sophisticated, more seductive. Her friend, McKenzie realized, had totally gone into the role.

'Tell your fortune?' McKenzie heard her ask Ted Pohl, a husky football player with a peace sign shaved into his crewcut. Before he had a chance to respond, Lilicat took his palm in hers and began the 'reading.' McKenzie wondered briefly if the fortune was as convincing as the costume. A few minutes later Lilicat was in Ted's arms, dancing to a slow song.

McKenzie turned as one of the guys draped in white passed by, carrying a bowl of popcorn. 'Chris?' she asked.

'Yo. Great costume, Mack. Very sexy.'

'Thanks.' She wondered briefly if there was anyone Chris Andreas *didn't* flirt with. 'Can I ask you a question? What are you guys supposed to be, anyway?'

'Snowflakes,' Chris told her solemnly. 'Three very large snowflakes.' He held out the bowl of popcorn, offering her some, and then moved on.

'I know this isn't a Charleston,' Aidan said, coming up beside her, 'but want to dance?'

McKenzie nodded, glad he hadn't asked her what she thought of Lilicat.

They danced to the slow song and three fast ones after that. All the while McKenzie kept an eye on Lilicat. She watched her go up to most of the guys in the room. Each time she'd take the boy's palm in her own. Each time the fortune-telling led to a dance, with Lilicat pressing herself close against her partner.

Maybe this is all an act, McKenzie thought, but Lilicat isn't usually much of an actress.

Breaking away from Aidan, she caught Lilicat between partners. 'Your costume looks fabulous,' she said. 'Where'd you get all that great jewelry?'

'Oh, hi, Mack,' Lilicat said, sounding distracted. She turned away from McKenzie and glanced behind her.

'Are you looking for someone?' McKenzie asked.

'Not especially.'

'So where did you find it?' McKenzie tried again, conscious of how stiff the question sounded. 'I mean, all the jewelry.'

Lilicat shrugged, her eyes still scanning the room. Why is she acting like I don't exist? McKenzie wondered angrily.

Someone changed CDs, putting on a rap song

and cranking up the volume. Carol Ann Licht, the *Guardian*'s news editor, who was dressed as a giant Dalmation, put her hands up in the air and began doing something that looked a lot like the hokey-pokey. Just about everyone stopped what they were doing; laughing, they watched Carol Ann. But Lilicat didn't seem to be conscious of any of it.

'Want to go into the kitchen?' McKenzie shouted over the music. 'So we can talk?'

A tall boy dressed as Frankenstein brushed by Lilicat, and she reached out and took his hand, trailing her fingers along the inside of his arm. Someone turned the music down. 'Want your fortune read?' Lilicat offered, smiling up into his eyes.

The boy stammered awkwardly as an equally tall girl stepped between them, removed his hand from Lilicat's, and led him off.

'Tell *my* fortune,' McKenzie said impulsively. She had to find a way to get Lilicat's attention. Maybe if she acted as if she believed this gypsy routine . . .

Lilicat took her palm and then dropped it with a hollow laugh. 'I forgot,' she said loudly. 'You have your own psychic powers. It'd be kind of a joke for me to read *your* future, wouldn't it?'

McKenzie felt herself go hot with anger. Lilicat and Aidan were the only two people she'd ever trusted enough to tell about her special ability – and she'd only done it because she knew they'd keep her secret. They'd both sworn they'd never mention it to anyone else, and now here was Lilicat discussing it with half the high school standing right there. 'You promised – ' McKenzie began.

But Lilicat never heard her. She was now standing in front of Aidan, holding his outstretched hand, running her fingers along his palm. Oh no, McKenzie thought. Not Aidan!

McKenzie realized with a sick feeling that the highwayman and the gypsy looked as if they belonged together. They seemed to have stepped out of the same dark folk tale.

Seconds later Aidan and Lilicat were dancing to a slow, romantic song. Lilicat's head rested on Aidan's shoulder. Then she pressed her body against his.

I'm not crazy, McKenzie thought. I have every reason to be jealous! She marched toward the dancing couple and pulled Lilicat away from Aidan. 'Excuse me,' she said in an icy tone, 'but what do you think you're doing?'

'I was dancing,' Lilicat responded angrily. 'This is a party. People dance together.'

'Not like you – ' McKenzie began, but before

41

she could finish Aidan stepped between them. 'Mack,' he said, 'what's the big deal? It was just a dance.'

Both of them were acting as if she were the one who was in the wrong. Standing there, surrounded by her classmates, McKenzie couldn't bring herself to accuse them of anything. It was just too humiliating.

'I want to go home,' she said with as much control as she could muster.

'Now?' Aidan asked.

'Now.'

Aidan scowled but said, 'If that's what you want.'

Lilicat watched, shaking her head. 'It's not even eleven and you're going home. Know something, Mack? You're a lot of fun.' She ran a hand down Aidan's back. 'You could always come back, you know.'

For a second McKenzie thought she was going to slap Lilicat. Instead, she made her way out of the house as fast as she could.

The night had grown cold and she shivered as she stood outside Aidan's car, waiting for him to unlock the door. I should have driven, she thought angrily. That way I could have left him here with his precious gypsy. Aidan came up behind her and unlocked the door. They got in silently, and neither spoke until they were far from Erin's house.

'All right, Mack.' Aidan's voice was calm but determined. 'Let's try this again – what happened in there? I mean, what exactly is the matter?'

'You didn't notice anything out of the ordinary going on at that party?'

'Not particularly, no.'

McKenzie sighed in disgust. Was he really that dense? 'If you don't know,' she finally said, 'I'm not going to be the one to tell you.'

'Oh, that's just great. Let's solve all our problems by refusing to talk about them.'

McKenzie remained silent for a bit, and then decided he was right. 'Okay,' she said. 'Lilicat was coming on to every guy at that party, including you.'

Aidan laughed. 'Come on, Mack!'

'I'm serious! She went up to every guy with that hokey fortunetelling routine and then wound up slow-dancing with them. Did you notice she wasn't telling fortunes for any of the girls?'

Aidan stopped for a light and shrugged. 'I wasn't really paying attention.'

'You certainly paid attention when she told your fortune!' McKenzie said indignantly. Then

43

curiosity got the better of her. 'What did she tell you?'

Aidan sent her a sly look. 'That I was in love with a high-strung flapper who was going to give me grief.'

'That's not funny!'

Aidan was chuckling. McKenzie gave up. She didn't speak again until he'd pulled up in front of her house. 'Are you going back to the party?' she asked. 'To dance with Lilicat?'

'I ought to,' Aidan muttered. 'It would serve you right.' Instead, he gave her a long, lingering kiss. But it didn't help at all.

McKenzie dragged herself up to her room, dropped the flapper costume on the floor, and changed into the faded red T-shirt she always slept in. She didn't know who made her the maddest – Lilicat, Aidan, or herself. She wouldn't be able to sleep, that she was sure of. She settled in the window seat, peering out into the night through the white gauze curtains. There was a faint 'Brrr' and her cat, Blue, jumped up beside her, purring.

'At least *you're* still my friend,' she said, petting his sleek black fur.

Blue purred his agreement. He settled himself in her lap, butting his head against her elbow.

McKenzie sighed loudly. 'Oh, Blue, what's happening to me? Am I totally paranoid? Did I just wreck two friendships?'

Blue, who was sound asleep, did not answer.

McKenzie stared out into the night. There'd never been a party that was such a total disaster. And she'd never felt so stupid and drained. She was barely aware of when her eyes drifted closed. Or when the dream began . . .

The figures are shadowy. A woman with wild red hair. A man. The woman is wearing a long skirt and a fringed shawl. The man is taller than she is, lean with sandy blond hair that hides his face. They are standing on a wooden porch surrounded by oak trees. Dusk is falling. The setting sun casts a red gleam along the porch's weathered floorboards. The man and the woman are standing close together, staring at each other. They speak in low voices. The wind sends oak leaves swirling down around their ankles. It lifts the edge of the woman's shawl and the hem of her skirt. She reaches out a hand, brushes it through his hair and down the side of his face. He says something to her.

She seems startled. She backs away a step, then looks down and turns away. He reaches for her, grabs her wrist, and turns her back to him.

Her bracelets glitter in the waning light. He puts both hands on her shoulders. She turns her head, angry. He takes her face in his hands, tilts it up, and kisses her.

She tries to pull away. But then she stops. She's lost in the kiss. She holds on to him as if she'll never let go.

The man reaches behind her, pushes open the door to the house. With his arms still wrapped around her, he leads the woman inside. They walk through a parlor. The walls are covered with flowered wallpaper. Tiny violets and green leaves. Gas lamps send shadows along the carpet. They pass through a living room. A dark green couch is set between two wing chairs. An embroidery hoop rests on a narrow end table. A needle dangles from it, swaying above the floor.

They enter the kitchen. The man sits at a rough wood table. The woman takes silverware and sets it before him. Her hand trembles. The heavy silver thuds loudly against the hard wood table. She reaches for a crystal glass on a high shelf. *Crash!* It shatters into a thousand pieces. But the woman doesn't seem to care. She reaches for another glass, which she sets on the table.

She takes a white bowl from the cupboard and spoons something into it from the pot on the stove. As the man begins to eat she fills his glass with wine – red wine – wine as red as blood. The man lifts the glass and drinks the dark red liquid. He eats heartily. The man is in danger. The danger surrounds him. It is everywhere, but he doesn't sense it. He continues to eat, never even glancing at the woman.

The woman turns away. She's searching for something in the cupboard. She finds what she wants and quickly hides it behind her back. She turns toward the man, smiling.

The man looks up and sees her smiling at him. He stands and takes the woman in his arms. He kisses her as if he is never going to see her again. The woman reaches up with one hand and brushes the hair out of his eyes, her hand trailing down his face.

Her other hand is behind her back – clutching a gleaming silver knife.

CHAPTER 5

McKenzie jerked upright, hitting her shoulder against the wall and waking up Blue. The cat made a cranky sound and jumped down from the window seat. It took McKenzie a moment to get her bearings. She was in her room, still on the window seat. Though the room was warm, she was shaking.

'This is crazy,' she said with a shudder.

She got up stiff-limbed and reached for the phone. She had to call Lilicat. She had to tell her about the dream. Lilicat would listen and make her laugh. Lilicat always calmed her down.

The phone fell from her hands as she realized she couldn't call Lilicat. Not in the middle of the night. Not after that party.

McKenzie bit her lip, fighting down an unexpected surge of pain. She couldn't bear to think that Lilicat wasn't her friend anymore. She wouldn't let herself believe that what had happened at Erin's party was real. And the truth was, it seemed far less real than the dream, the dream that was still with her.

Determined not to forget any of the details, McKenzie reached into her backpack and took out the pocket tape recorder she used for reporting. Then she began to retell the dream as carefully as she could.

McKenzie slept late that morning. When she woke up, it was nearly noon. In the kitchen she found a note from her parents, saying they'd gone to the local mall to buy her brother a winter coat. McKenzie smiled, wondering what they'd promised Jimmy to get him to go shopping. Trying to get eight-year-old James Gold into a clothing store was like trying to get Blue to go swimming.

She poured herself a glass of juice and a bowl of cereal, and sat down at the kitchen table to read the Sunday paper. She was still half asleep, not ready to deal with all that had happened the night before. Tell that to her brain. She couldn't stop thinking about it. Lilicat and Aidan. Was there really something going on between them?

And what about the dream? She couldn't ignore it, but she didn't know what to make of it either.

McKenzie was startled out of her thoughts by the sound of the doorbell ringing. She ran a hand through her sleep-tangled hair, hoping that whoever it was would go away. The doorbell rang again. 'All right, all right,' she grumbled. 'I'm coming!'

Belting her robe securely around her waist, she opened the front door. Aidan stood there, gazing at her with steady gray eyes. 'Morning, Mack,' he said quietly.

'Hi.'

'I feel lousy about what happened last night,' he said.

'Me too,' McKenzie admitted.

He looked past her toward the living room. 'Mind if I come in? I think we ought to talk.'

McKenzie nodded. They sat down on opposite ends of the living room couch. 'This is ridiculous,' McKenzie said.

Aidan gave her a sheepish smile and moved to the center of the couch. 'Better?'

McKenzie returned the smile and moved a few inches closer to him. Still, she felt as if there were a wall between them.

'So . . .' Aidan began.

'So?'

'Don't go getting mad again, but I honestly don't know what set you off last night,' he confessed. 'I mean, how can you take one dance so seriously?'

McKenzie hesitated. She couldn't exactly accuse him of being in love with her best friend. Not when he was sitting six inches from her, obviously trying to work things out. 'I know it was just one dance,' she said at last. 'But didn't Lilicat's behaviour last night seem, I don't know – weird – to you?'

'It seemed drunk to me,' he replied.

'Lilicat doesn't drink.'

'Didn't you see that idiot Kurt Brown pouring a bottle of something into the punch?'

'No,' McKenzie admitted. She'd been too busy watching Lilicat.

'Well, he did, and I'll bet anything Lilicat had a little more punch than she should have. She's probably got a major headache right now.'

McKenzie turned this over in her mind. It was possible, she supposed. But she couldn't believe that was the whole story. 'I've got to ask you a question,' she said carefully. 'What made you decide to be a highwayman instead of a gangster?'

Aidan shrugged. 'Gangsters wore suits, right?'

He grinned at her. 'You know about my wide selection of suits.'

McKenzie smiled in spite of herself. Aidan had never owned a suit in his life and at this rate, never would. He had taken her to last year's junior prom wearing a tuxedo jacket, a T-shirt, jeans, and high-tops.

'I didn't have one,' he continued, 'and my dad flat out refused to lend me one of his. So I hit the secondhand stores, and I still couldn't find the right suit. But I saw this great cape and the boots really cheap. I figured highwaymen were sort of earlier versions of gangsters.'

McKenzie still wasn't satisfied. 'Did you know Lilicat was going to be a gypsy?'

'Why would I?' He tugged on a strand of her hair. 'Unlike some people I know, I don't spend a lot of time discussing what everyone is going to be wearing to the latest social event.'

'Oh, shut up,' McKenzie murmured, but she was finding it hard to remain angry with him. She wondered if she should tell him about her dream and seeing blood that day in the hallway. No, she decided, not until she could make some sense of it herself.

'Look, Mack.' Aidan's voice was earnest. 'I'm sorry about last night. I guess I wasn't taking

Lilicat seriously. I really didn't understand why you were getting so worked up.'

'I'm sorry too.' McKenzie held out her hand, a peace offering. 'Friends again?'

Aidan took her hand and drew her to him. 'It'd better be more than friends,' he muttered. He held her close for a moment, looking into her eyes with an intensity that told her that he wanted her every bit as much as she wanted him. He bent his head. His lips came down not on hers, but on the side of her neck, sending shivers through her.

'Aidan,' McKenzie breathed.

'Mmmm?'

'It's the middle of the day.'

'You want me to stop?' he asked, moving up her neck to a tender place behind her ear.

'No,' she answered truthfully. 'No.'

McKenzie was at school earlier than usual on Monday morning. She wanted to make sure she got there before Lilicat, which really wasn't difficult. Lilicat was always at least five minutes late. Straightening things out with Aidan had made McKenzie determined to apologize to Lilicat. After all, no matter how bizarre Lilicat had been acting, she had been the one who'd made a scene.

She walked down the hall, weaving through the morning throng of students, her eyes automatically checking the faces for Lilicat. As she might have guessed, Lilicat was nowhere in sight.

McKenzie got her books from her locker, slamming it shut as Ted Pohl came up to her. 'Hey, Mack, did you finish Friday's English assignment?'

Their teacher, Mr. Wright, had asked them to write an essay on what would have happened if Hamlet had managed to kill his stepfather in the first act of the play.

'I did it last night,' McKenzie answered.

Ted grinned. 'Me too. It was my shortest essay ever. I wrote, "There wouldn't be any need for the other four acts." '

'I think Mr. Wright may have been looking for a little more than that,' McKenzie told him, smiling. 'But you've got a point. Have you seen Lilicat today?'

'Nope.' Ted moved off down the hall. 'Catch ya later.'

McKenzie made her way to her friend's locker and stood there waiting as the homeroom bell rang. This was probably the hundredth time she'd been late for homeroom because she'd waited for Lilicat. Thank goodness, her home-room teacher wasn't a nut about punctuality.

The halls were nearly empty when Lilicat sauntered into school. McKenzie had been staring at the floor, counting scuff marks on the linoleum tiles. She looked up suddenly. Lilicat was coming toward her, wearing the silk gypsy shawl and dramatic black eyeliner. McKenzie's body went hot. Despite the cool morning air, sweat instantly soaked through her clothes.

The party's over, McKenzie thought. Why is she still wearing that costume?

Lilicat drew closer, and McKenzie felt a band of fear tighten around her chest. Lilicat had managed to put on the makeup in a very familiar way. Heavy and dramatic, it was an exact double of Vanessa Grant's.

'Lilicat,' McKenzie said uncertainly. She was getting hotter by the minute. It was as if the temperature of the air around her had just shot up to over a hundred. She wondered how long she could remain near Lilicat before passing out.

'What?' asked Lilicat, opening her locker.

McKenzie was determined to go through with it. 'I – I wanted to apologize for Saturday night.'

Lilicat looked at her as if she were from Mars.

'I'm sorry if I made a scene at Erin's party,'

McKenzie explained, feeling even more miserable.

Lilicat shut her locker and spun around as Chris Andreas passed by. 'Hey, Andreas,' she called. 'Wait up. I want to talk to you.'

Chris stopped, smiling broadly as Lilicat joined him.

McKenzie just stood there, shaking. Apologizing to Lilicat for the scene at the party had been hard for her. But she'd done it because she cared about their friendship. And Lilicat hadn't even bothered to listen.

Lunchtime couldn't come soon enough, as far as McKenzie was concerned. She'd agreed to meet Aidan, and after the morning's encounter with Lilicat she wanted to see him desperately. She wanted to complain to him about Lumpy and chemistry, to tease him about the fact that he was in dire need of a haircut. She was sure that seeing Aidan would make her feel like things were still relatively normal. She headed for his locker.

Aidan stood beside his locker, gazing down at Lilicat. The hundreds of other kids streaming through the halls, changing classes, faded into a blur in the background. The two of them were talking intently. Again McKenzie felt a flash of jealousy. She fought it down quickly. Jealousy made her uncomfortable. She didn't want to feel this way about her two closest friends. Still, she couldn't help wondering what they were talking about.

A tingling sensation ran along the length of her spine. The feeling wasn't jealousy, she realized. It was her special sense, trying to warn her of something. Something that she'd rather not know.

McKenzie's vision was changing. Aidan and Lilicat now took on a peculiar sharpness, as if she were seeing them through one of Aidan's closeup lenses.

Behind Aidan and Lilicat, someone opened a classroom door. The fringed edge of the silk shawl began to flutter in the breeze. Transfixed, McKenzie stared at the scene before her. She began to shiver as she realized that there was something all too familiar about the way Lilicat and Aidan were standing. Aidan leaned forward to whisper something to Lilicat, and she reached up and brushed the hair out of his eyes, her hand trailing down his face.

Oh, my God, McKenzie thought, trembling with horror. Lilicat and Aidan are acting just like the two people in my dream!

CHAPTER 6

'Mack.' Erin Livingston's voice behind her made McKenzie jump. 'Are you okay? You're shivering. I've got a sweater in my locker – do you want to borrow it?'

McKenzie turned to Erin. She had been startled out of her vision. But was that a good thing? 'I – I have a jacket in mine,' she said. 'I was just going to get it.'

Erin stepped back, her green eyes showing concern. 'You and Aidan left early Saturday night. Is everything all right with you guys?'

'Fine,' McKenzie lied. 'I was just tired – I'm probably coming down with a cold or something. How did the rest of the party go?'

Erin smiled. 'Well, you missed Lilicat trying to teach Bob Kowalski to dance, but that was about as wild as it got.' She glanced down the hall at Lilicat. 'Is she still wearing that shawl? I mean, it's pretty and all, but it's not Lilicat's usual style.'

Thank goodness! McKenzie thought. I'm not the only one who's noticed. Still, what could she tell Erin – that Lilicat was redoing her wardrobe? Instead, she asked about something else that had been bothering her, something she hadn't dared ask Aidan. 'Erin, did Aidan go back to your house after he dropped me off? I lost an earring, and he said he'd look for it. I keep forgetting to ask him whether or not he ever did.'

'Not that I know of,' Erin said, 'but I can look for it when I get home tonight. What does it look like?'

McKenzie described an earring she'd never had, and Erin left promising to check the house for it. McKenzie felt ridiculously grateful that Aidan hadn't gone back to the party.

Her eyes returned to his locker. Lilicat was gone. He stood alone, his sandy head bent as he spun his combination lock. Everything back to normal.

McKenzie thought uneasily of the vision she'd just had. It was definitely warning her of something – something connected to Lilicat and Aidan and her dream. Were they both in danger?

Should she tell Aidan what she'd seen? She
didn't know how to do it without sounding
totally unreasonable and possessive. And right
now she needed things to be right with Aidan.
She needed that too badly to risk another fight.

McKenzie stuffed her books back into her
locker and grabbed the freshly washed sweats
she'd brought to school that morning. Lilicat
hadn't been at lunch. McKenzie hadn't seen her
since the morning. But they had gym class
together, and now McKenzie was steeling herself for a heart-to-heart talk. Somehow she had
to make Lilicat realize that she was in danger.
She had to make her listen.

She hurried through the halls, only to be inter-
cepted by Lumpy Johnson. 'Mack,' he said, snag-
ging her arm. 'I need to ask you something.'

'Ask me later,' McKenzie said, pulling her
arm free. 'I've got gym now.'

'This is important,' he insisted.

'All right.' McKenzie sighed. There was no
use fighting the inevitable. 'What's so
important?'

'I need you to cut a hundred words off your
column this week.'

'You what?'

Lumpy shrugged apologetically. 'Coach just

told me about an unscheduled track meet. They're bringing in a guest team from Canada. I've got to cover it, and I'm all out of space on the sports pages.'

'I am not going to cut my column,' McKenzie told him, smiling sweetly. 'Why don't you cut some of the football coverage? Or learn to write without using so many macho metaphors?'

Lumpy stared open-mouthed, and she walked away fuming. She'd come dangerously close to telling him how awful she thought his column was. Lumpy always made it sound as if Lakeville's teams were fighting World War II all over again. They were always shooting at the enemy, bombing the other team, or taking no prisoners. It was all so silly she could barely believe it.

But why was she getting so irritated? She hurried toward the gym. The first bell had already rung. McKenzie figured she had about a ten percent chance of changing into her gym suit and making it into the gym before the final bell. She was almost relieved when she realized she had no chance of having that talk with Lilicat.

She dashed into the locker room, performed a lightning change, and headed for the gym.

She stopped when she saw Lilicat in the next aisle. Lilicat was leaning against one of the equipment lockers, the embroidered shawl draped over a closely fitting black top and a short red skirt. She was talking to Judy Jerome, an outrageously flirty senior whom she normally stayed away from.

'It's going to be a primo frat party,' Judy was saying. 'All of the hottest guys at Emden are going to be there.'

Emden? McKenzie realized they meant Emden Junior College. The school was only about ten miles away, but neither she nor Lilicat had ever considered going to one of the frat parties. The frats at Emden had a reputation for being pretty crude.

Lilicat was studying her fingernails. McKenzie saw that they were painted black with tiny gold crescent moons. 'Exactly how hot are the Emden guys?' Lilicat asked Judy as the second bell rang. 'I mean, Lakeville is getting boring fast.'

'What do you think of John Osga?' Judy asked.

John Osga had graduated from Lakeville last year. He looked like a rock star and drove a souped-up Trans Am. He was also a total egomaniac slime. McKenzie nearly choked as Lilicat wrote down her number on a piece of notebook paper and handed it to Judy. 'Tell him to call me.'

McKenzie knew Lilicat almost as well as she knew herself. And she knew something was radically wrong. 'Hey, Lilicat,' she said, hoping she sounded casual. 'Are you going to change for gym class?'

'I'm thinking about it,' Lilicat answered.

'I'd better go,' said Judy. 'See ya, Lilicat, Mack.'

McKenzie didn't even acknowledge her. 'Lilicat,' she said, 'ever since Erin's party you . . . you haven't been acting like yourself. Would you please tell me what's wrong?'

Lilicat gave her an impatient glance. 'Nothing – except you keep asking me what's wrong. I'm fine. Okay?'

'No,' McKenzie said, 'it's not okay. I'm worried about you. I've had . . . a dream and a really scary vision. . . . I think you may be in danger.'

'I see,' Lilicat said slowly. 'You're worried 'cause I told Judy I'd go to an Emden party, right?'

'You used to think those guys were animals,' McKenzie reminded her. 'Especially John Osga!'

Lilicat shrugged. Her silk shawl was catching the reflection of the overhead fluorescent lights. It shone. 'Maybe I don't think the same way anymore.'

'Why not?'

'Because I'm tired of not having a boyfriend,' Lilicat said. She began to sort out the tangle of bracelets on her left wrist. 'I know what I'm doing, Mack. You don't have to get all over-protective, like a mother hen or something.'

McKenzie felt a flash of hurt, but she forced herself to try again. 'Lilicat, the other day in school, I had a vision of you and – '

Lilicat cut her off, laughing. 'Do you want to hear one of *my* visions? I had a vision of me and the man of my dreams falling insanely, wildly, deliriously in love.' McKenzie felt herself go cold as Lilicat continued, 'And I swear I'm going to make that vision come true.'

'No.' Alarmed, McKenzie reached out and touched her friend on the shoulder.

Nothing could have prepared her for what happened next. With one hand Lilicat removed McKenzie's hand from her shoulder. With the other she pushed her. Surprised, McKenzie stumbled against the locker.

'Don't you touch me,' Lilicat hissed.

Tears stung McKenzie's eyes. She wasn't hurt – except for her feelings. Some part of her just couldn't believe it. The Lilicat she knew would never do this to her.

'What's going on here?'

Blinking back tears, McKenzie looked up to see Ms. Lyons, their gym teacher, standing at the entrance to the locker room. 'I'm surprised at you two,' the teacher went on. 'This isn't like you.' Ms. Lyons checked her watch with a show of impatience. 'You've got exactly two minutes to get changed and onto the gym floor. And Caine, wash that makeup off your face.'

McKenzie went through gym class numb with hurt. She couldn't even bear to look at Lilicat. She was losing her best friend. Or maybe she'd lost her already.

They were putting away the field hockey sticks when Lilicat came up alongside her. 'That has got to be the dumbest game,' she said. 'All of us smacking each other in the shins with wooden sticks. I think the last time I actually hit the ball was back in junior high.'

McKenzie turned to her, afraid to trust what she'd just heard. Was the old Lilicat really back?

Sure enough, there was Lilicat, wearing her familiar blue sweats, smiling and waiting for McKenzie to agree that field hockey was indeed the dumbest game.

Suddenly the truth dawned on her. She knew exactly what was wrong with her friend! Right now Lilicat wasn't wearing the makeup or the jewelry or the shawl. She was just standing there in a Lakeville gym suit, acting totally normal. It was only when she wore the gypsy costume that she acted so weird. It's the costume, McKenzie thought. She felt so horrified that it was difficult to breathe. Whenever Lilicat wears the clothes she bought at the flea market, she's not herself. She becomes someone else!

CHAPTER 7

'**Lilicat,' said McKenzie** as they left the gym and headed for the locker room. 'Will you do me a favor?'

'It all depends,' Lilicat teased.

'This is serious,' McKenzie insisted. 'When you get dressed, don't put on the shawl.'

Lilicat put her left foot up on a wooden bench and began untying her sneaker. 'Why not?'

'You won't believe me when I tell you. Just trust me on this one, okay?'

Lilicat rolled her eyes. 'Is this' – she looked around, noticed the locker room full of girls – 'that thing I promised not to discuss? You know, your strange ability?'

'Yes,' McKenzie said. 'Now stop talking about it – you're making it sound like something dirty.'

Lilicat giggled. 'All right,' she said. She took the shawl out of her locker and stuffed it in her daypack. 'I'll humor you.'

'Thank you.' McKenzie felt almost weak with relief. 'Now will you do something else for me?'

'Mack, you have got to let me put on the rest of my clothes. I am *not* walking out of here in my sweats.'

'That's not what I was going to ask.'

Lilicat shrugged herself into her top. 'All right, but you only get three wishes. After that I vanish.'

McKenzie knew her friend was kidding, but somehow the words were chilling. Considering what had been going on lately, she was in no mood to joke about spells or vanishing. 'Just two wishes,' McKenzie said, trying to match her friend's joking tone. 'The second one is, I want you to go back to the flea market with me on Saturday.'

'No can do. I've got a game.'

'We'll go after the game. You can cheer your heart out.'

The locker room emptied around them as Lilicat finished dressing. McKenzie noticed she hadn't put on the heavy make-up or the bangle bracelets. 'Why do you want to go back there?'

68

Lilicat asked. 'We don't have another costume party coming up, do we?'

'No. We have to find Vanessa Grant.'

Lilicat looked at her as if she'd lost her mind. 'Why,' she asked patiently, 'do we have to find Vanessa Grant?'

'Because there's something very weird about those clothes she sold you.'

Lilicat looked at her blankly.

'When you wear them, you're not yourself,' McKenzie explained.

'Who am I?' Lilicat's voice was amused.

'I'm not sure. But whoever it is, she's kind of weird. She comes on to all these guys – guys like Mark McConnel – and that's all that matters to her.'

Lilicat's eyes widened in astonishment. 'I did that?'

'And whoever she is, she's connected to something really strange and violent,' McKenzie went on, determined to get the worst over with. 'I had this nightmare and a horrible vision. I can't quite put the pieces together, but they all involve blood or a knife.'

Lilicat shuddered. 'You think I'm in danger?'

McKenzie nodded. 'And I'm sure it started with Vanessa Grant. That's why we have to find her. Before my visions become real.'

'All right,' Lilicat said quietly. 'We'll go Saturday, after the game.'

McKenzie sat high in the bleachers, watching Lakeville sweep the fourth quarter of their game against Cedar Ridge. Her eyes were repeatedly drawn to the sidelines where Lilicat, in her green-and-white uniform, stood with the other cheerleaders.

McKenzie wondered about her plan to return to the flea market. She wasn't sure what would happen when they found Vanessa Grant, but she was determined to get some sort of explanation. Now another thought occurred to her. Vanessa Grant was dangerous, she was sure of it. Was it a good idea to meet with her a second time? Maybe they would only make things worse.

A warm hand covered her eyes. 'Guess who.'

'Give it up, Collins,' she said. 'I'd know your voice anywhere.'

Aidan removed his hand and squeezed in beside her on the bench, a camera dangling from his neck. 'Good game, huh?' he asked, eyes on the field. Aidan was in his photographer mode, which meant he was slightly hyper, alert every second so as not to miss the perfect shot.

A roar from the crowd drew her attention back to the game. 'We're creaming them, right?'

McKenzie had never been too big on football. It was only recently that she'd figured out that touchdowns were a good thing.

'Basically,' Aidan agreed. 'I hate to admit it, but even though Andreas is always telling everyone how incredible he is, he *is* incredible.'

McKenzie squinted down at the field. All football players looked alike to her. Aidan snapped a few shots, cursed, and said, 'I'm too far away. Why do you want to sit a mile from the field, anyway?'

McKenzie shrugged. 'I like it up here.'

'Well, I need to be somewhere where I can get a decent photo or I'll never hear the end of it from Lumpy. Do you want to come down to the sidelines with me?'

McKenzie took one look at the crowded area below them and shook her head. 'No thanks. I'll see you later.' She gave him a quick kiss.

McKenzie grinned and settled back to enjoy the end of the game. She was actually on her feet cheering when Ted Pohl made the winning touchdown. Within seconds, two of the linebackers were carrying Chris Andreas on their shoulders, and Lilicat was in the middle of another gravity-defying jump. McKenzie let the excitement in the stands sweep over her, feeling grateful for the break from her problems.

Later, she threaded her way down the bleachers and met Lilicat at the side of the field. 'Ready to go?'

Lilicat shook her pompoms at her. 'As long as we don't get back too late. Ilene isn't around today, and Gill may want company.' Ilene was Lilicat's mother, and Gillian was her twelve-year-old sister. Their elder sister, Elizabeth, was away at college.

'No problem,' McKenzie told her. 'We'll be home before dinner.'

'Then let's ride,' said Lilicat, heading for the car.

'You'll never guess who called me last night,' Lilicat said as McKenzie pulled out of the stadium parking lot. 'The most inflated ego ever to graduate from Lakeville – John Osga! He thought I wanted to go out with him. Me! With him! How does this sort of thing happen to me?'

'You really don't know?' McKenzie asked.

'Don't tell me. One of the guys on the team gave him my number.'

'Try Judy Jerome.'

'Judy Jerome? How did she – '

'You gave it to her,' McKenzie answered. 'You wrote down your number, handed it to her, and told her to have John Osga call you.'

Lilicat opened her mouth, then closed it. 'When I was wearing the shawl?' she asked in a very small voice.

McKenzie nodded.

'We'd better find Vanessa Grant fast,' Lilicat said, 'before I wind up married to Mark McConnel.'

McKenzie turned off the winding country road and onto the farm drive where the flea markets had been held. The oak and maple trees had turned even more glorious shades of red and gold since the girls' last visit, but Mack was in no mood for scenery. The drive was empty. There were no stalls, no crowds, no rows of cars parked in the sun.

'It's gone,' McKenzie said.

'Certainly looks that way,' Lilicat agreed.

'Now what?'

'We go home and I change out of this uniform,' Lilicat suggested.

McKenzie shook her head. 'We have to find Vanessa Grant. I'm convinced she's the key to this whole mess.'

Lilicat sighed. 'We could try the phone book under Grant.'

The phone book didn't sound very promising to McKenzie, but she didn't have any better ideas. They drove to the nearest diner.

Lilicat ordered milk shakes. McKenzie found the phone book. There were, as she'd suspected, about sixty Grants. None of them had the first name Vanessa or the first initial *V*. Maybe she's married to Alex Grant, or she's his sister, McKenzie thought, dialing the first number listed. She tried to remember if Vanessa Grant had worn a wedding band. She'd worn so many rings it was impossible to tell.

Alex Grant answered and told McKenzie there was no Vanessa there. So did Anna Grant, Arthur Grant, Bascombe, Belinda, and Betty. McKenzie got answering machines for Alexander and Benjamin Grant. She'd used up all her change, and that didn't even get her through the letter *B*!

She returned to the counter.

'No go?' Lilicat guessed.

'How much change do you have?'

'Drink your shake and let's go home,' Lilicat advised. 'At least we can make the phone calls cheaper.'

'I guess,' McKenzie agreed. She had a feeling that they weren't going to find Vanessa Grant with a few phone calls. 'What's this?' she asked, pointing to a newspaper in front of Lilicat.

'A newspaper,' Lilicat replied, deadpan.

'Can I see?'

Lilicat shrugged and handed her the paper.

McKenzie turned to the section that advertised things like used furniture. 'Aha!' she said triumphantly.

'Aha?'

McKenzie pointed to a boxed ad at the bottom of the page. 'Devon Flea Market – Saturday, October 25th, 9 a.m. to 5 p.m. – corner of Hastings Road and Rider's Way.'

'It moved,' Lilicat said. 'It's the same flea market in a different location.'

'They do that sometimes. Now all we have to figure out is where Hastings intersects Rider's Way.'

In the car Lilicat took the map out of the glove compartment and navigated. 'We're in for a ride,' she predicted. 'The place where Hastings crosses Rider's Way is nearly in Cedar Ridge. It's almost twenty miles from here.'

McKenzie glanced at the gas gauge. 'We can make it.'

'It's probably not a good idea for me to go into Cedar Ridge territory in a Lakeville cheerleader's uniform,' Lilicat worried. 'Especially after the game today.'

'I'll protect you,' McKenzie promised.

'Can't we just swing by my house so I can change?'

That was the second time Lilicat had asked to go home and change, and it worried McKenzie. What if what Lilicat really wanted was another chance to put on the costume? 'Sorry,' McKenzie said firmly, 'your house is out of the way.'

They arrived at the flea market almost half an hour later. This time the market was set in a big, open field. McKenzie felt a surge of relief as she saw the familiar spread of tables and racks.

'There's my pig!' Lilicat said, heading straight for the metallic flowered piggy bank.

By the time McKenzie'd caught up with her, she'd put a nickel in the bank, and the pig was attempting to speak French.

'Isn't this great?' Lilicat asked. 'No one else bought it. I think it's meant to be my pig.'

'Buy it already,' McKenzie advised.

Lilicat happily bought the pig and they moved on, searching for the gypsy. They visited every booth in the flea market twice over. There was no sign of the red-haired woman.

'She's not here,' McKenzie concluded.

'Then let's ask someone where we can find her.'

McKenzie and Lilicat spent the next twenty minutes going from stall to stall, describing Vanessa Grant and her booth. No one had heard of her.

'This doesn't make sense,' McKenzie said. 'Vanessa Grant was too eccentric for anyone to forget. If she was part of this flea market, someone here would know her.' She looked at Lilicat doubtfully. 'Did I dream the whole thing?'

'If you did, then I had the identical dream. Come on, there's still a few people we haven't tried.' Lilicat stopped at a stall belonging to a man who sold antique jewelry. 'Excuse me,' she said, 'but we're looking for a Vanessa Grant. She had a stall in this flea market when you were at Hoffstater's Farm a few weeks ago.'

The man looked up at them with a sharp gaze. 'She isn't part of this flea market.'

'But she was,' McKenzie insisted. 'She had red hair and she sold used clothing. Her stall had a big oval mirror and all sorts of old dresses and jackets.'

'And a hatrack,' Lilicat put in. 'There was a cast-iron hatrack right in the front of it.'

'She told us she used to work in the theater as a wardrobe mistress,' McKenzie added. 'Lilith bought a gypsy costume from her.'

The man rocked back on his heels. 'Well, you're right about that. She did do a stint in the theater, quite some years ago.'

'It must be the same person,' Lilicat said eagerly. 'She wore lots of makeup, right?'

'Sometimes,' he replied.

'Then you know her,' McKenzie pressed.

'*Knew* her,' the man answered. 'Vanessa Grant died in a fire three years ago.'

CHAPTER 8

'Excuse me,' Lilicat said, her voice suddenly shaky. 'But could you repeat that?'

The man who sold antique jewelry squinted at her, as if trying to decide whether she was hard of hearing. 'I said Vanessa Grant's been dead three years,' he repeated. 'She died in a fire.'

'Where?' McKenzie asked.

'Don't know. We set up one fall and she was part of the market. We closed for winter and when spring came around again, we heard she'd died. Never got any of the details.'

'You're sure?' McKenzie asked.

He nodded.

Lilicat had gone very pale. 'This Vanessa Grant,' she said. 'She had long, red wavy hair, wore lots of jewelry . . .'

'That's the one,' he confirmed.

'Come on,' McKenzie said. 'If she's been dead for three years, then how come we saw her three weeks ago?'

'Obviously, she's not dead,' Lilicat said quickly. 'Someone else died in the fire.' She turned back to the man. 'Whoever told you she died got it wrong.'

The man picked up a quartz brooch set in silver. He held it up to the sun so that it caught the light; the brooch cast rainbows all along the table. 'You're being logical,' he told Lilicat. 'And there's nothing wrong with that except that Vanessa Grant wasn't a creature of logic. She didn't play by the rules. Not any of them.'

McKenzie studied the man's eyes. He must be lying. Perhaps he was trying to protect Vanessa Grant and steer them away from her. McKenzie concentrated, trying to sense what he was up to. It didn't always work, but sometimes when she concentrated hard, she could almost hear a person's thoughts.

The man gazed back at her with steady, dark eyes. What she felt in him was pure calm. He wasn't lying. A second impression came to her then, one she didn't quite understand – this man knew a great deal more than he would ever put into words. He wasn't going to tell them everything he knew about Vanessa Grant, and for good reason. McKenzie saw that whatever it was he knew, he was certain it would scare them to death.

'I don't understand,' Lilicat said. She was sounding more and more upset. 'What are you trying to tell us?'

The man broke eye contact with McKenzie, giving Lilicat a sympathetic glance. 'I'm telling you that Vanessa Grant died in a fire three years ago. And that despite all that, there's a real possibility you met her – or the likes of her – three weeks ago.' He drew a black velvet pouch from his shirt pocket and slipped the quartz brooch inside. 'And that's all I have to say on the subject, except if you see her again, stay away. She's not a good one to tangle with. Never was.'

'But – ' Lilicat and McKenzie said together.

The man ignored them, turning to a customer and explaining the history of an opal ring.

'There's got to be someone else here who knew her,' McKenzie insisted.

'Mack.' Lilicat's voice was faint. 'Is it okay if we just go home? This is getting a little weird.'

McKenzie looked at her friend. Lilicat was still unusually pale. 'Just give me another ten minutes, okay?'

They tried every other dealer in the Devon

flea market, but they couldn't find anyone else who knew Vanessa Grant. Finally, McKenzie turned to Lilicat, resigned. 'I have a feeling we're not going to get any more information.'

'Okay by me,' Lilicat said quickly.

They got into the car. Lilicat was staring out the windows with dark eyes. 'I don't mean to keep asking this,' McKenzie said, 'but are you all right?'

'I'm fine.' Lilicat played nervously with one of the pleats in her skirt. 'Mack . . . you said you've seen visions about this costume thing, right?'

McKenzie nodded, and turned the key in the ignition.

'What exactly did you see?'

McKenzie told her, careful not to make it sound as if Lilicat were trying to steal Aidan from her. She knew that the Lilicat who sat beside her now would never do that.

'My God, I'm turning into someone who'd try to steal her best friend's boyfriend!' Lilicat said when McKenzie had finished.

'No,' McKenzie said at once. 'It's not *you* who's doing that. It's the costume that's making you act that way.'

Lilicat was quiet for a while. McKenzie had

driven halfway to her house before she said, 'This is really serious, isn't it?'

'I think so,' McKenzie replied. She didn't want to scare her friend, but she couldn't lie to her either.

'What do you think that man meant when he said it's possible that Vanessa Grant's dead, and it's also possible we saw her?'

' "Or the likes of her," ' McKenzie quoted. 'And there was also that bit about her not playing by the rules. I don't know what any of it means,' she admitted ruefully. 'It's all like some giant riddle.'

Lilicat shivered. 'Do you think we saw a ghost?'

McKenzie rejected the idea at once. There were no such things as ghosts, except in movies and books. Then again, if she hadn't had them herself, she'd say there were no such things as dreams that predicted the future. She'd sure learned that those existed. So maybe . . .

'Mack,' Lilicat repeated, 'do you think we saw a ghost?'

'I don't know,' McKenzie told her. 'I don't know what we saw when we met Vanessa Grant.'

'What are we going to do?'

The answer in her head was, 'I have no idea.'

She thought for a moment. 'I'm not sure about what comes next, but the first step is obvious. We get rid of that costume.'

To her relief Lilicat nodded. 'As soon as we get back to my house. When Halloween comes around, I can be Bart Simpson like everyone else!'

For the first time since they met Vanessa Grant, McKenzie felt better. Her dreams and visions had been warning her and now she'd listened to them. More important, she'd finally gotten Lilicat to listen as well. She was going to put an end to the trouble before it got any worse.

Lilicat picked up the piggy bank, which she'd put on the car floor. 'Well, it wasn't a total waste. At least I got my pig.'

'It was worth it all for the pig,' McKenzie agreed, grinning.

She turned onto Lilicat's street, where a mess of Halloween decorations had gone up during the week. One house had a row of jack-o'-lanterns on the porch. Another had crepe paper black cats in every window. 'They all look like Blue,' McKenzie said, 'except skinnier.'

'Mack, can you speed it up?' Lilicat's voice was taut with fear.

'We're on a residential street, Lilicat. The speed limit is twenty-five.'

'Forget the speed limit!'

'Lilicat,' McKenzie began, 'why – ?'

And then McKenzie saw why. A police car was parked in front of the Caine house, its lights flashing.

'Oh, my gosh,' said Lilicat in a stricken voice. 'Gillian is home all alone!'

CHAPTER 9

'**What if something's** wrong with Gill!' Lilicat squeaked.

'It may not be anything serious,' McKenzie said reassuringly. She hoped she was right.

McKenzie knew that Gillian was often in the house alone, and no one had ever thought twice about it – like all the Caines, she was extremely independent and good at taking care of herself.

McKenzie parked directly across from the police car. The front door of the Caine house was wide open. She and Lilicat raced inside.

They found Gillian sitting on the living room couch, sobbing. On either side of her was a uniformed police officer.

'Gillian!' Lilicat cried, rushing to her sister's side. 'Are you all right?'

'Who are you?' asked one of the policemen.

'I'm Lilith Caine, Gillian's sister, and this is my friend McKenzie.'

'Are your parents around?' asked the second officer. 'I'm afraid we haven't been able to get much information out of your sister.'

Gillian, McKenzie saw, was nearly in hysterics. She let Lilicat hold her, but she buried her head against her shoulder, refusing to look at anyone.

'Our mother's away on a business trip,' Lilicat explained. 'And our dad hasn't been around for years – he and my mom split up a long time ago.'

The first policeman, whose name was Officer Howard, wrote all this down.

McKenzie wanted to ask him why they were there, but she suddenly felt dizzy. It was as if something at the very edges of her vision were *moving*. Something she couldn't quite see. She sat down, waiting for whatever it was to either become clearer or pass. She barely heard the rest of the discussion between Lilicat and the police officers. All of her senses were focused on – on what?

It was something at the very edge of the room. Although the windows in the room were shut, the curtains were moving ever so slightly, as if touched by a breeze. McKenzie stared as the breeze, if that's what it was, seemed to cross the room and move toward her. It lifted a piece of paper on the coffee table and set it down again at an angle. It rippled through Officer Howard's hair. Then McKenzie felt it – cold and yet impossibly soft; it passed across her face like a piece of silk. It only lasted a second. Then it was gone.

McKenzie felt herself reeling. She had no words to describe what had just happened. All she knew was that something else had been in the room with them. And whatever it was, it meant them harm.

Seconds later, her vision returned to normal, and the dizziness passed. The only people in the room were the police officers, herself, and the two sisters.

'You still haven't told us what happened,' Lilicat was saying. She rubbed Gillian's back, trying to comfort her.

Officer Howard sighed. 'About a hour ago 911 got a call from your sister here. She said someone had broken into your house. She was calling from your next-door neighbor's.'

Lilicat bit her lip. 'And?'

'We scoured this house top to bottom,' the other officer replied. 'We checked the yard, we checked with your neighbors. We can't find any signs of a break-in. The house hasn't been touched.'

'Gillian,' Lilicat said gently, 'what did you see? What made you call the police?'

But Gillian just sobbed quietly, refusing to answer.

'She was crying like that when we got here,' Officer Howard went on. 'Maybe we should get a doctor and find out if she's been hurt.'

'I wasn't hurt!' Gillian mumbled into her sister's sleeve. 'No one touched me.'

'Then what happened?' McKenzie asked. She knew Gillian wasn't the type to scare or cry easily. She wondered if it was possible that Gillian had sensed what she herself had felt. No, she decided. If Gillian had had a similar experience, she wouldn't have reported something as real life as a break-in.

Again, Gillian just shook her head, refusing to answer the question.

Officer Howard stood up. 'I honestly don't know what else we can do. Are you kids going to be all right if we leave you here?'

'Gill?' Lilicat asked.

Gillian nodded.

'We'll be fine,' Lilicat answered. 'Besides, my mom's coming home later tonight.'

'All right then.' The two officers gave Lilicat

a number to call in case she needed them, and left.

For what seemed a long time Lilicat sat with Gillian huddled against her side. The younger girl finally calmed down and wiped her tear-streaked face. 'Now,' Lilicat said, 'will you please tell me why you called the police?'

'I thought someone broke into the house.'

'Why?' McKenzie asked. 'Did you hear some-thing or see something?'

Gillian stood up. 'I want a drink of water.'

'I'll get you one,' Lilicat offered.

Gillian gave her a look that said she clearly thought her sister was being ridiculous. 'I can get my own water,' she told them, heading into the kitchen.

McKenzie and Lilicat followed her. 'When was the last time you had anything to eat?' Lili-cat asked.

Gillian shrugged. 'I had a peanut butter sand-wich around noon.'

'Then I have an idea,' Lilicat said in a fake cheerful voice. 'Mack and I will start some dinner. We can make your favourite – steak. Why don't you go upstairs and get some rest? I'll call you when it's ready.'

'No,' Gillian answered. She folded her arms

across her chest in a stubborn gesture that McKenzie knew all too well from Lilicat.

'No?' Lilicat echoed.

'I'm not going anywhere near your room.'

'What's my room got to do with anything?'

'It's next to mine,' Gillian pointed out. 'And that's too close.'

'What on earth are you talking about?' Lilicat asked. She was obviously losing patience fast.

'Your room is where I saw her,' Gillian answered.

McKenzie suddenly understood what had happened. She asked anyway. 'Who's "her"?'

Gillian had gone very white. 'The woman with the red hair.'

CHAPTER 10

Lilicat shot McKenzie a panicked look. 'I think we'd all better sit down.' Gently, she pushed Gillian into one of the kitchen chairs. 'Now,' she said when she and McKenzie were also sitting at the table, 'tell us about the woman with the red hair.'

'I don't want to talk about it,' Gillian replied.

'Gill, this is important,' McKenzie said. 'Lilicat and I have seen her too, though never in the house. We need you to tell us what you can.'

Gillian sent Lilicat a cunning look. 'Will you let me borrow your suede vest?'

'I'm going to strangle her,' Lilicat said to McKenzie.

'Let her borrow the vest,' McKenzie advised.

Lilicat sighed. 'All right, brat, you can borrow the vest. *For one day only.*'

'And your INXS tape?'

'And the tape. Now tell us about the red-haired woman.'

Gillian hesitated a moment, then began. 'I was in the living room. I was actually vacuuming. Mom is always saying we don't do anything around the house unless we're asked. I thought I'd surprise her. It was really noisy. You know how that vacuum sounds, like it's going to explode or something. I guess that's why I didn't hear it at first.'

'Hear what?' McKenzie asked.

'Noises coming from upstairs, from Lilicat's room. When I shut the vacuum off, it sounded like someone was walking around up there. First, I told myself it was either the chestnut tree rubbing up against the house or the house settling. Then I decided a raccoon had gotten inside. Finally, I told myself I was imagining things. But the noise didn't stop.' Gillian was talking in a low monotone. She had been doing so ever since she'd started the story. It didn't sound anything like her normal voice, and it made McKenzie uneasy.

'I decided I was being silly. That there was nothing to be afraid of.' Gillian's eyes met her sister's. 'So I went upstairs. The door to your room was open. And there was a woman standing in there. She had long, red wavy hair. She wore all this heavy makeup and about a trillion pounds of jewelry. And she had a long skirt and a silky blouse and your denim jacket.'

'Tell me that last part again,' Lilicat said.

'She was wearing your denim jacket. And admiring herself in your mirror. It was – I don't know – creepy.'

McKenzie felt the chills run through her again. 'It's more than creepy.'

'That's when you went next door and called the police?' Lilicat asked.

Gillian nodded. 'I got out of the house as fast as I could. I couldn't stay in there with her. I didn't want her to see me.' She shrugged, looking slightly embarrassed. 'After I called the police I just got all shaky and started crying.'

Lilicat reached for her hand. 'You did the right thing. If you ever see that woman again, just get away as fast as you can.'

'Who is she?' Gillian asked.

'Her name is Vanessa Grant,' McKenzie replied. 'That's all we really know right now. Lilicat, I want to have a look at your room.'

Lilicat shuddered but said, 'All right. I guess we have to.'

McKenzie and Lilicat went upstairs, leaving Gillian in the kitchen. McKenzie entered first.

She wondered if she would be able to sense anything that might help her stop the red-haired woman.

At first glance Lilicat's room looked untouched. Her schoolbooks were stacked neatly on her desk. Her dresser top was covered with the usual array of makeup, jewelry, and perfume.

Lilicat headed straight for her closet. 'It's gone,' she reported in the same flat tone Gillian had used. 'She took my denim jacket.' She walked over to the alcove where her bed was.

McKenzie could only see her friend from the back, but it was clear that Lilicat's entire body had just gone rigid with fear. 'Lilicat,' she said, 'what's wrong?'

Lilicat just pointed to the bed where the pieces of the gypsy costume were spread out, as if someone were about to put them on. 'I didn't leave them there,' she said, her voice trembling. 'They were in my closet. She took them out. Why would she do that?'

'I don't know exactly,' McKenzie said, trying to keep her voice calm. It was important that she level with her friend. 'But I know she wants to hurt you. I think she wants you to wear the clothes and become whatever it is you become when you do.'

Lilicat backed away from the bed. 'This is really sick.'

'We'd better finish checking out the room,' McKenzie said. 'I want to be sure that she didn't take – or leave – anything else.'

For the next hour McKenzie and Lilicat searched the bedroom. They checked every shelf, emptied every drawer, and nearly took apart the closet. McKenzie even moved the bed; Lilicat wouldn't go near it.

'Everything's the way it usually is in here,' McKenzie finally concluded. 'I don't think she touched anything else.' She walked over to the open window and gazed out into the branches of the chestnut tree.

Lilicat came to stand beside her, hugging herself as if for warmth. 'Somehow I'm not comforted.'

McKenzie stared down at the rain gutter below. 'Lilicat,' her voice took on a note of hope, 'do you see what I see?'

'My denim jacket!'

'But what's it doing down there?' McKenzie wondered.

'Maybe she escaped through the window.'

'It's a two-story drop to the ground. And the branches of the tree are too far away to climb.' So how did the jacket wind up hanging from the rain gutter? McKenzie wondered. Had the arrival of the police startled Vanessa, so that she'd thrown the jacket out the window? Or maybe, as Lilicat had said, she'd fled through the window. It was impossible to tell.

'How am I going to get my jacket down?' Lilicat wondered.

'Do you have a long ladder? Maybe you can climb up there and get it. I'd volunteer, but you know what I'm like when it comes to heights.'

'I think there's one in the garage.' Lilicat turned suddenly from the window. 'You know what? I'll get someone to climb up there and get it down tomorrow. Right now I don't even want to think about this anymore.' She went to her closet, rummaged through it, and emerged with a plastic bag. Taking the costume from the bed, she began stuffing it into the bag. 'Let's get rid of this thing once and for all.'

'An excellent idea,' McKenzie agreed.

'The question is, how?' Lilicat shuddered. 'I don't even want to touch it.'

McKenzie didn't blame her. In fact, she thought, it really wasn't a good idea for Lilicat to touch the costume. Reluctantly, McKenzie held out her hand. 'Why don't you give it to me? I'll take care of it.'

'What are you going to do?'

McKenzie shrugged, taking the bag gingerly. 'Burn it?'

'Where? Lakeville has all sorts of laws against burning leaves and garbage. Maybe we should throw it out.'

McKenzie shook her head. 'No, that's not thorough enough. If even a scrap remained, it could probably do major damage.' She thought for a minute. 'I know. I'll drop it off at the dump on my way home.'

Lilicat looked at her doubtfully. 'You don't mind having it in the car with you?'

'I'll lock it in the trunk.' McKenzie smiled at her friend. 'Don't worry, Lilicat. I'll get rid of it. I promise.'

Dusk was falling when McKenzie drove away from Lilicat's house. Great, she thought, it'll be dark by the time I get to the dump. The town dump was on the outskirts of Lakeville at the very end of Calvary Road. It was a part of town that made McKenzie feel as if she'd reached the end of the world. She'd only been there once before when her father decided to get rid of an unusually large metal sculpture, the one her mother had called a master disaster. The dump had given her the creeps then, and she'd been with her father – in broad daylight.

Now as McKenzie turned onto Calvary, she tried not to think about her destination. The way there was bad enough. Calvary Road was lined with broken-down bars and movie houses that specialized in porn flicks. She passed the last of the bars and turned on her brights. In the total darkness, McKenzie felt lost on the unlit road.

For a while there was nothing on either side of her. Just stretches of empty road. Then she began to see the first of the junkyards. Large metal shapes loomed high behind barbed-wire fences. McKenzie knew that by daylight these would be rusted-out cars and trucks. Now they looked like dark, sinister creatures from an alien planet. Stop imagining things, she told herself firmly. Dealing with this costume is weird enough.

She reached the end of Calvary sooner than she thought she would. Maybe she remembered it as being farther. Maybe she just didn't want to get out of the car.

She pulled onto the dirt road that led to the dump. It had rained recently, and the road was badly rutted. The Toyota jounced along, rattling so hard McKenzie's hands shook on the steering wheel. She brought the car to a stop in front of the wire fence that enclosed the dump. The gate was padlocked. Why hadn't she expected that? Did she really think they'd leave it open at night?

Reluctantly she got out of the car, keeping the headlights on; she wasn't going to do this in the dark. The first thing that hit her was the smell – sour and decaying. The odor mingled with the cold night wind. She could feel it surrounding her, seeping into her clothes, clinging to her skin.

Shivering, McKenzie unlocked the trunk and reached for the plastic bag containing the costume. She hesitated. It hadn't burned her when she'd taken it from Lilicat. There was no reason to think it would burn her now. She shrugged and picked it up. No problem. She looked at the gate surrounding the dump. It was about ten feet high. She'd just toss the bag over the top.

She approached the gate slowly. There was a big, dark lump in front of it. McKenzie figured someone else had left their garbage there. And then the lump moved.

McKenzie screamed as she realized the lump was a man. He got to his feet, shielding his eyes against the glare of her headlights. He was filthy. Long, greasy hair hid most of his face. His clothes were black with grime.

He was probably homeless, McKenzie

realized, but that didn't make him any less frightening. She backed away. All she had to do was get to the car, she told herself. Just get back into the car and you'll be safe.

The man took a step toward her, dazed. McKenzie screamed again. He mumbled something, then turned and lumbered off into the darkness.

For a long while McKenzie stood there shaking, her fists clenched so tightly that her fingernails dug into the palms. She felt the plastic bag in her hand. She had to get rid of it. Again she approached the fence. She threw the bag as high as she could. It landed beside her. Something scuttled by her feet and she jumped, shrieking. Oh, God, she realized, it's a rat. She listened carefully, and could hear small squeaks and clicking sounds coming from the pile on the other side of the fence. The place was filled with rats.

Swallowing hard, she picked up the bag again and threw it as hard as she could.

The bag caught on the top of the fence. And hung there.

There was no way out of it. She was going to have to climb the gate. She fitted the toe of her sneaker into one of the openings in the fence and grabbed on with her hands. The metal was cold and slimy. She held on tightly and began climbing. The fence creaked and swayed under her weight. She couldn't be much more than four feet above the ground, and already her fear of heights was kicking in. Her mouth was dry and the dizziness was starting. Still, McKenzie climbed. She felt something tickle the back of her hand. Her hand flew back off the gate, and she nearly fell. She fought back a shudder. It was just a roach, she told herself. They can't hurt you.

She was becoming more and more freaked. She wasn't sure how much longer she could do this. She thought of Lilicat, took a deep breath, and forced herself to keep climbing.

At last she reached the top of the fence. Heart pounding, McKenzie heaved the bag into the darkness beyond. She heard it land with a soft rustle, heard the rats squealing as it hit.

She scrambled down the fence and sprinted to the car, locking herself in. Only then did she let herself enjoy the sense of relief that washed over her. She'd gotten rid of the costume. Lilicat was safe.

CHAPTER 11

Lilicat sat alone in her room. It had begun raining an hour ago. Now it was nearly midnight. The rain was whipping itself into a storm. Sheets of water battered against her window. The wind sounded as if it would rip the house from the ground. Lilicat tried to ignore what was going on outside. She concentrated on the last problem of her math homework.

She jumped at a deafening crack of thunder. The house shook. She was the only one on the top floor. Gillian was camped out with their mother. Ever since she'd seen Vanessa Grant, she'd refused to sleep in her own room.

Lilicat squinted at her notebook. Solving this last equation was taking forever. She kept getting things wrong. Each time she had to go back to the beginning and start over.

A strong gust of wind hit the side of the house. The floor beneath her feet shuddered. And then her bedroom window blew open. A blast of cold rain hit her. She had to close the window. Slowly, she made her way to it. A tingling sensation played along her spine. She ignored it. It was nothing more than a chill.

She stopped about a foot from the window. An icy wind gusted into the room. Needles of rain stung her. The tingling sensation intensified. Lilicat wondered if a storm could be evil. Could it be more than wind and rain?

She stepped to the window and reached out to grab hold of the two windowpanes. She swore under her breath. The long white curtains were in the way. They flapped wildly, tangling themselves around her neck. Soaking wet, they clung to her neck and arms.

Lilicat struggled to untangle herself. The sodden material tightened around her head and throat. She couldn't pull it off. She couldn't see. She couldn't even scream . . .

She yanked the curtains from her face. And stared at the material. It wasn't white muslin. It was the embroidered silk shawl!

Lilicat screamed. Tried to run. She fell hard on the wood floor. The shawl tightened. It cut across her throat. She could barely breathe. It was strangling her.

A streak of lightning lit the sky. Vanessa Grant's husky voice filled the room: 'No use fighting it. Now you belong to me!'

McKenzie sat bolt upright in bed, sweating and shaking. 'Lilicat,' she said aloud. She could see Lilicat, thrashing on the floor of her room, having the life squeezed out of her by the shawl. And worse – being taken over by Vanessa Grant.

Bright morning sunlight poured in through McKenzie's bedroom window, and she realized that what had seemed so real was over. It was a dream. But was it?

McKenzie had had other dreams come terrifyingly true. No way, she reassured herself. The shawl couldn't strangle Lilicat. She'd thrown it into the dump. Quickly she glanced outside. There *had* been a storm last night. The ground was soaked and littered with branches. Which meant Lilicat might be . . .

Grabbing the phone, McKenzie punched in Lilicat's number.

'Hello?' McKenzie didn't recognize the voice that answered.

'Is Lilicat there?'

'Lillian?'

'No, Lilicat – Lilicat Caine.'

There was a moment of perplexed silence, then the woman's voice explaining, 'Actually, we call our cat Thomas Jefferson.'

McKenzie groaned, apologized for calling a wrong number, and hung up. She punched in the number again. This time Mrs. Caine answered the phone.

'Ilene,' McKenzie said with relief. Lilicat and her sisters all called their mom by her first name, and so did most of their friends.

'Good morning, Mack.'

'I'm sorry for calling so early, but I really need to talk to Lilicat. Is she there?'

'I'm sorry – you just missed her. She breezed out of here about five minutes ago. She said something about an early cheering practice.'

'At the school?'

'I believe so.'

'Okay, thanks. I'll catch up with her there.'

McKenzie grabbed some jeans, Aidan's sweater, and a pair of boots from her closet. She put them on quickly, barely stopped to brush her teeth and hair, and raced downstairs.

'Whoa!' said her father, intercepting her in the hallway. 'You're not even going to eat breakfast? What, may I ask, is the rush?'

McKenzie thought for a moment before

answering. 'I've got a history test today. A bunch of us are meeting for a breakfast study group. You know, to test each other and all.'

Her dad raised his hands in surrender. 'Far be it from me to interfere with studiousness.'

'Thanks, Dad,' she said, giving him a quick kiss. She felt a twinge of regret at having lied to him. Her parents were so warm and loving and – safe. She wished she could sit down with them, eat breakfast, and not worry about anything more important than getting to school on time!

She was out the door in a flash and at the school in record time. Was there really a cheering practice? she wondered. If there was, she'd probably find Lilicat in the gym.

Lilicat, however, was not in the gym. She was sitting in the school parking lot on the hood of Mark McConnel's car. McKenzie's heart sank at the scene before her. Lilicat's hands were resting lightly on Mark's shoulders, her head bent towards his. He pulled her toward him and kissed her hard. His hand reached up, tangled itself in Lilicat's hair, and held her in place as he kissed again. He acted like he owned her.

That would have been bad enough, but it wasn't what was sending chills through McKenzie's body. Last night she had driven to the end of Calvary Road, climbed the fence at the town dump, and gotten rid of the gypsy costume.

And now Lilicat was sitting on the hood of Mark McConnel's car, wearing the embroidered silk shawl.

CHAPTER 12

McKenzie **watched in** dismay as Lilicat let Mark McConnel pull her from the hood of his car; she stood pressed tight against him. The silk shawl shimmered in the morning sun. Never in a million years would Lilith Caine have let that creep get so close to her. Not the real Lilicat. But the girl who wore the shawl put her hand into Mark McConnel's back pocket and walked with him into the school.

McKenzie knew exactly what this meant. Getting rid of the costume was real. But so was her dream. The costume had returned through some sort of magic. Not only that, it looked like Vanessa Grant had taken over her friend. Lilicat was in major danger.

There's got to be something I can do, McKenzie

thought frantically. There's got to be some way I can reach her.

She followed Lilicat and Mark into the school and waited until they'd separated and headed for their own lockers. Seconds after Lilicat slammed her locker door closed, McKenzie caught up with her. 'Wait a minute,' she said. 'I have to talk to you.'

Lilicat raised one eyebrow. She was wearing the makeup again. Her eyelashes were nearly stuck together with thick black clumps of mascara. 'Not now, Mack. I've got to get to homeroom.'

McKenzie couldn't hold back her feelings anymore. 'You've got to listen to me! You almost died last night!'

Lilicat stared at her in disbelief. 'What *are* you talking about?'

'I saw what she tried to do to you with that shawl. She nearly strangled you! How can you wear it? How can you? I took it to the dump so this would never happen again, remember?'

'Mack, will you calm down – you're making a scene!' Lilicat looked exasperated. 'I mean, we're standing in the middle of the entire school. Besides, how dare you even talk about throwing away my clothes? I'm crazy about this shawl – and so are all the guys.' She gave

McKenzie a long look. 'I get it. That's why you're having this fit.'

'Why?' McKenzie's voice was shaking.

'It's obvious. You can't take seeing all these guys pay so much attention to me.'

'You can't be serious! Don't you see what's going on? You're in danger! I'm worried about you, Lilicat!'

Lilicat raised her eyes to the ceiling, obviously bored by the entire topic. 'You're worried about me.'

'I am.'

'What you mean is you're jealous.'

McKenzie took a step back. She knew it wasn't the real Lilicat she was dealing with, but the accusation still cut. 'How can you say that to me?'

'It's time someone told you the truth,' Lilicat replied. 'You're used to being the one who has the gorgeous, adoring boyfriend. And now things have changed. Now all the guys in the school are paying attention to me – including *your* gorgeous, adoring boyfriend. You can't take it, can you?'

McKenzie took a deep breath, trying to hold on to her temper. 'The problem,' she said slowly, 'has nothing to do with jealousy. The problem is that shawl. Last night I drove ten miles and threw it in the town dump. Do you want to tell me how you got it back?'

Lilicat shrugged. 'You must have thrown something else away. It was in my room this morning.'

McKenzie tried again. 'Lilicat, when you wear it you don't act like yourself. I mean, do you really like Mark McConnel?'

'He's not so bad. I like having guys pay attention to me. What's wrong with that?'

'Nothing,' McKenzie told her patiently, 'except you're out of control. I'm scared, Lilicat. This is more than flirting. The costume is changing you. Something awful is going to happen. I can feel it.'

Lilicat stared back at her; her dark eyes were flat. 'I can take care of myself, Mack.'

'You don't even know what – '

'Aidan!' Lilicat cut her off in midsentence. She left McKenzie standing there explaining things to the locker while she moved down the hall toward Aidan.

McKenzie watched as he turned to Lilicat, and his face lit with a smile. She hooked her arm through his and began to walk toward her homeroom.

McKenzie felt her own anger flare and then die down. Lilicat was in danger. And no matter how awful she acted, McKenzie was determined to save her.

Day after day, McKenzie watched her friend with growing fear. First Lilicat stopped wearing her own clothes. She wore the gypsy costume to school every single day. She wore so much makeup McKenzie barely recognized her. She was getting more and more into the role of the gypsy, McKenzie was sure of it. Lilicat flirted with every boy in the school. She nearly glued herself to Aidan's side whenever he was in sight. Three different times, McKenzie tried to approach her friend, and each time Lilicat brushed her off. Her voice was louder, her gestures more exaggerated. McKenzie couldn't believe it when Lilicat started to cut classes. She ignored her schoolwork. She pierced her left ear twice and was wearing big gold hoops.

Then again, there were times McKenzie thought that *she* was the crazy one. The other kids seemed to think Lilicat's behavior was either funny or just bizarre. Except for Lumpy Johnson looking positively alarmed when Lilicat sat in his lap one day at lunch, nobody seemed all that bothered by the way she was acting.

At one point McKenzie pulled Aidan aside.

She wasn't going to accuse him of anything, but she needed a reality check. 'Aidan,' she asked, 'have you noticed a change in the way Lilicat's been acting?'

Aidan looked at her.

'I mean, she's obsessed with that costume she wore to Erin's party. She hasn't taken it off all week. And she's not acting like Lilicat. It's . . . weird!' McKenzie shook her head. 'It's beyond weird. It's spooky.'

Aidan gave a good-natured shrug. 'Everyone's entitled to act out now and then. She's not hurting anyone, is she?'

McKenzie wanted to reply, 'She's hurting me,' but she couldn't admit that to anyone.

'Mack . . .' Aidan hesitated. 'Don't take this wrong or anything, but maybe you're being a little too . . . you know, sensitive.'

His words stung. That was her problem. She *was* too sensitive – too sensitive to things that other people didn't see or feel. Sometimes it felt as if there was this whole other world that was open to her, a world that no one else even knew about. And now it was going to destroy her best friend.

McKenzie's own schoolwork was suffering. She had a column due the next day that she hadn't even thought about. She could barely bring herself to talk to Aidan, who flirted with Lilicat and then accused her of being too sensitive! And she was having trouble sleeping. There was part of her that was scared to sleep – terrified of what the next dream might bring.

To McKenzie the changes in her best friend were horrifying. And then she heard Boz Bosley, Aidan's best friend, introducing Lilicat to a boy who'd just transferred to Lakeville. 'Keith Jaffe, this is Lilith Caine. But most of us call her Lilicat.'

'No one really calls me Lilicat anymore,' Lilicat demurred. 'Most people call me Vanessa.'

'Huh?' Boz grunted. 'What are you talking about?'

Keith extended his hand. 'Hey, Vanessa, how are you doing?'

McKenzie felt as if the floor were collapsing beneath her. It's complete, she thought. Vanessa Grant has taken her over.

'Vanessa, wait,' she said, thinking maybe it would help if she played along.

'Vanessa' turned her back on her and walked away.

McKenzie grabbed Lilicat's silk-clad arm. Suddenly it felt like her hand was on fire. Lilicat jerked away, her voice a low hiss. 'Don't touch my shawl!' Before McKenzie could say a word, Lilicat hurried off down the hall.

McKenzie clutched her hand and moaned.

Totally dismayed, she looked down. Her hand was covered with blisters.

CHAPTER 13

That evening **McKenzie** sat cross-legged on her bed, listening to the tape recording she'd made of her dreams. She was trying desperately to fit the pieces of the puzzle together. She shut off the tape recorder and consulted her cat, who was curled up on her pillow, intently washing his toes.

'Okay, Blue, listen up,' she began. 'First I had that vision of Lilicat and Aidan in the hallway, and it looked like there was all that blood.'

Blue stopped cleaning his toes long enough to look at her with interest.

Encouraged, McKenzie went on. 'Then I dreamed of this man and woman. They sort of argued and then wound up kissing like mad. But then the woman took out a knife and hid it behind her. And that last dream.' She shuddered. 'Vanessa Grant nearly killed Lilicat. But the thing is, it looks like she got inside her head instead.'

The cat rubbed up against her hand, wanting to be petted. She drew her hand back, wincing. The blisters throbbed.

'Let's try it this way,' she said, petting him with her other hand.

'So,' she continued, 'does this stuff even connect? If Vanessa Grant really died three years ago, then the woman Lilicat and I met was . . . I don't know . . . a spirit or ghost. And that spirit is possessing Lilicat – through the costume!'

Blue licked the end of her finger, and she scratched him under the chin. 'You're a sweet cat, but you're no help.'

She heard the doorbell ring downstairs, and then heard Jimmy shout, 'Maaaaack . . . it's lover boy!'

McKenzie felt her face go bright red. There were many times she wished Jimmy went to boarding school. This was definitely one of them.

'Maaaack – ' he started again.

'I'll be right there!' she shouted back before he repeated the full announcement.

She checked herself quickly in the mirror. Except for her hand, she didn't look too awful.

She went downstairs, wondering why Aidan had shown up. She found him in the middle of a Nintendo game with Jimmy. 'So that's why you came over.'

Aidan laughed. 'That's right. I love you for your brother's Nintendo.'

McKenzie sighed. 'Let me know when it's over. I need some fresh air – I'll be out on the porch.'

Aidan joined her a few minutes later.

'That was quick.'

'Your mother told Jimmy he had to do his homework.'

'Ah. So, what's up?'

Aidan leaned against the porch railing. 'You and I haven't really seen that much of each other lately. I missed you.'

McKenzie felt a rush of warmth at his words, and yet they weren't enough to reassure her.

'Besides,' he went on, 'I wanted to bring you this.' He held out a tape. 'It's an Irish band, sort of Celtic rock. I figured you needed some culture.' Aidan, whose family had emigrated from Ireland two generations earlier, was currently into Irish bands. He was forever making her tapes, as if trying to convert her.

McKenzie took the tape. 'Thanks.'

'I guess I should have called before coming

119

over,' Aidan said, sensing her wariness. 'Did I interrupt anything?'

'Only me worrying about Lilicat. I think she's in trouble, Aidan. I'm scared for her.'

'What do you mean?'

'I've been trying to tell you.' McKenzie winced at the impatience in her voice, but it wasn't as if this was the first time she had tried to talk to Aidan about Lilicat. 'You know that gypsy costume Lilicat's been wearing nonstop?'

He frowned. 'The one from the party?'

'It's more than a costume. It's got some sort of power over Lilicat. When she wears it, she changes.'

'That again!' Aidan said with a groan. 'Look, I know Lilicat's been acting a little wild. But it's not exactly the end of the world. Besides, she's smart. She'll straighten herself out.'

McKenzie was about to reply but Aidan stopped the argument by taking her in his arms and giving her a long, slow kiss.

It was impossible for McKenzie not to respond. She'd missed him, too. Her arms wound behind his neck as she pressed herself against him – and they both collapsed onto the porch swing.

'Sorry.'

Aidan gave a low, throaty laugh. 'There's

nothing to be sorry about.' He pulled her closer and stopped suddenly. He took her hands in his and turned them over, examining them gently. 'Mack, what happened? Did you burn yourself in the kitchen or something?'

McKenzie took a deep breath and told him the truth. 'It happened this afternoon at school. When I touched Lilicat. She was wearing the shawl.'

He looked at her questioningly.

McKenzie's words came out in a rush. 'We bought that costume at a flea market from a woman named Vanessa Grant. When we went back a few weeks later to try to find her, we were told she's been dead for three years. And I've been having dreams and visions . . .'

'Mack – '

'And there's always blood or violence in them.'

'Shhh. It's all right.' Aidan was stroking her hair, trying to soothe her.

'No, it's not all right!' McKenzie's voice was growing increasingly shrill. 'There have been other things. Lilicat gave me the costume so I could get rid of it. I drove all the way to the town dump, climbed the fence, and threw it in. And she's got it back, Aidan. She said she just

121

found it in her room the next morning. And she's calling herself Vanessa!'

Aidan said nothing, just held her close.

'Don't you believe me?'

Aidan sighed. 'I know you wouldn't lie about this stuff. And I know that you see things other people don't see. But Mack, even you've got to admit this sounds pretty far out.'

It did, and McKenzie knew it. She wasn't going to be able to convince him. Aidan continued to hold her, but she sat stiff in his arms. The close feelings of a few moments earlier were gone.

'Maybe I'd better go,' he said at last.

'I guess.'

'I'll call you later. Take care of your hand, okay?'

She nodded, fighting back tears. She watched his loose, easy walk as he headed away from the house. Lilicat had become a stranger. Aidan wouldn't even listen to her. And they were both in mortal danger.

McKenzie had never been so frightened. And she had never felt so alone.

'Jimmy, have some string beans,' Mrs. Gold said that night as the family sat at the dinner table.

'Mack, have some string beans,' Jimmy mimicked. He was always trying to get McKenzie to eat all the vegetables so that he wouldn't have to eat any.

McKenzie didn't respond. She was thinking about Lilicat, about what might happen and what she could do to stop it.

'Mack,' her mother said, 'you're not eating.'

McKenzie blinked, and glanced at the food on her plate. Obediently, she began eating.

Her father cleared his throat. 'So,' he began in a cheerful voice, 'how's high school these days?'

McKenzie looked at him blankly.

'High school,' he repeated. 'You know, that tan brick building you supposedly spend five days a week in.'

McKenzie gave him a reluctant grin. 'I know what it is, Dad. High school is . . . it's okay.'

'Okay,' he repeated in a thoughtful tone. 'That's a very descriptive answer, especially from a writer. Conveys a great deal of information.' His tone was teasing, but McKenzie felt herself stiffen. The last thing in the world she needed right now was the third degree from her parents.

'Your father's right,' her mother added. 'You've barely had two words for us all week. Is something wrong, honey?'

McKenzie heard the concern in her mother's

voice and felt herself torn. Part of her wanted to tell them what was wrong so badly. And the other part of her knew she couldn't bear it if they, too, thought she was crazy. 'I've just had a lot of schoolwork this week,' she said. 'And tomorrow's Friday. I've got my column due. I don't mean to be rude or anything, but could I be excused now?'

Her parents exchanged glances, and then her mother said, 'Go ahead.'

In her room McKenzie sat at her desk, trying to force herself to write the column. But although she genuinely thought the student council should have more say in the curriculum, she couldn't bring herself to write a single paragraph about it. It just seemed so – unimportant.

This is ridiculous, she told herself sternly. I've got to turn this thing in tomorrow. Maybe music would help. Sometimes if she put on headphones, she found the music and whatever she was writing sort of blended together. It was easier to get into the writing. The only question was, what did she want to listen to? She saw the tape Aidan had given her that evening sitting on her desk. With a shrug, she slipped it into her Walkman and returned to the computer. 'It's vital that the student council have a say in Lakeville's curriculum . . .' she began.

McKenzie had nearly finished the first draft of her column when a song on the tape snapped her concentration. It was a new version of the old ballad 'The Wraggle-Taggle Gypsies.' She remembered learning the folk song in elementary school. The lyrics told of a woman who leaves her husband, house, and land to run away with the gypsies. Her husband rides all night to find her, and when he does, he asks how she could give up her life with him. The woman's reply ran through McKenzie like lightning.

. . . What care I for my house and land?
What care I for my money, O?
What care I for my new-wedded lord?
I'm off with the wraggle-taggle gypsies, O!'

She turned away from the computer screen, shaking. She saw Lilicat in her green-and-white cheering uniform, arcing high into the air for the sheer joy of it. And then she saw her giving all that up. She saw her as the gypsy, as she'd been at Erin's party, the wild-haired gypsy, telling fortunes, trying to draw every boy in sight into some invisible web. She saw her no longer as Lilicat but completely transformed. . . .

The wild-haired woman stands in the kitchen. She piles dishes into a large metal tub. At the table the fair-haired man pushes his empty plate aside. He gets up, his chair scraping against the wooden floor. He stands behind the woman. He puts his arms around her waist, bends his head, whispers something in her ear. She turns in his arms, but not before she hides something in the folds of her skirt. He picks her up. She laughs and wraps her arms around his neck.

He carries her out of the kitchen and into the hallway. They pass through the arched doorway of an alcove. Still carrying her, he begins to climb a steep flight of stairs. The wall along the stairs is papered with pink roses. Her long green skirt trails over the wooden banister. Beneath it she wears black lace-up boots. Laughing, she rumples his hair. Her bracelets click against each other like coins.

He reaches the landing. A candle burns in a wall sconce, throwing shadows on the faded carpet. She lifts the candle from the sconce. He crosses the landing and continues up, past the second floor to the top of the stairs. The attic door is made of four wooden boards, nailed together with a crossbar. He kicks it open.

He sets the candle in a candleholder by the door. He carries her to the far end of the room, to a big bed tucked beneath the sloping eaves. The last red glow of sunset streaks across the floorboards. She tugs on his hair and whispers something in his ear. He drops her on top of the patchwork quilt. He reaches for her. She scrambles away. She crosses to the far end of the attic. She takes an embroidered silk shawl from a peg and wraps it around her shoulders. She lights other candles. One is in a wrought-iron candleholder set on the floor. One is on top of a small mahogany dresser. With her back to him, she pulls a knife from inside her skirt and holds it under her shawl.

At last she turns to him. She takes his hand and draws him to her. 'I've waited for you,' she says. She runs a hand along his cheek, caressing him. 'For two years I've worked as a servant, lived in this attic. I gave up my job with the theater. All so I could be here for you.'

She draws his head down to hers. 'I've been dreaming of this for so long,' she tells him. They lock in a passionate kiss. The kiss goes on for a very long time. She slowly pulls the knife out from behind her back. She raises it high in the air over his head. And plunges it down into his back. He cries out and tries to wrench away, the knife still in him. She pulls it downward. Blood wells out of the wound and streams down the man's white shirt. It coats his black vest. It streams down his arm. It paints his wrists and hands deep red. He stumbles and falls to his knees. The woman laughs and steps away from him. She holds the knife high in the air. Like the knife's blade, her hands are red with his blood.

McKenzie jerked against the back of her chair, bringing herself back into the present. She was sweating and chilled at once, feverish from her vision. She knew she had to do something. Right away. She went to the phone and began to punch in Lilicat's number. Then she stopped, hung up, and dialed the Caine family number instead. This time she prayed Mrs. Caine would answer the phone. She had to tell her to take the gypsy clothes when Lilicat was alseep – take them and destroy them!

McKenzie waited as the phone rang four times. Her heart sank as the machine picked up. 'This is the Caine residence. No one can take your call right now . . .'

McKenzie didn't dare leave a message. Even if she said something as vague as asking Mrs. Caine to call her, Lilicat would be suspicious. What can I do? she wondered.

She called seven more times that night. Each

time she got the machine. At last, exhausted, McKenzie fell asleep.

Early the next morning McKenzie headed straight for Lilicat's homeroom. She pushed through the crowded halls, wondering dimly why Lumpy Johnson was wearing a Groucho nose and mustache. Then she realized it was already Halloween.

Lilicat did not show up in her homeroom. Not even fifteen minutes after the third bell had rung. Her panic rising, McKenzie headed for the pay phones. She dialed the Caines' number, hoping against hope that her vision of the night before was just some tired daydream that didn't mean a thing.

'Hello?' Mrs. Caine answered the phone, sounding unusually nervous. 'Oh, McKenzie, thank God it's you! I just left a message at your house. Have you seen Lilicat?'

'That's why I was calling you,' McKenzie admitted. 'She didn't show up for homeroom this morning. I thought maybe she was home with the flu or something.'

'I wish she was.' Mrs. Caine spoke slowly, as if she didn't want to say what she was saying. 'Lilicat went out late last night without telling me. She never came home. I've called the police. They said they'd get back to me. Oh, Mack, what am I going to do? Lilicat's disappeared.'

CHAPTER 14

McKenzie gripped the phone receiver so tightly her knuckles whitened. Lilicat was gone. And there was no doubt in her mind that her best friend was now completely possessed by the spirit of Vanessa Grant. Vanessa Grant would destroy Lilicat. She had to find her before it was too late.

'Ilene,' she said, 'I know this is going to sound like a weird request, but would it be all right if I came over today and spent some time in Lilicat's room?'

'I'll be here,' Mrs. Caine answered.

'Thanks. I'll be over as soon as I can.' McKenzie hung up. Now how was she going to get out of school? She couldn't very well walk into the office and explain that her best friend was being possessed by an evil spirit. She could cut school, but Lakeville had recently gotten very tough about that – McKenzie wasn't ready to explain to her parents that she'd been suspended because she was following her instincts. She was just going to have to stick it out and get to Lilicat's as soon as school was over.

'Who knows the origin of Halloween?' asked Mr. Wright, McKenzie's English teacher.

Who cares? she thought. She'd never felt less enthusiastic about the holiday. Or school, for that matter.

'The candy companies started it so they could make lots of money,' answered Ted Pohl.

'Not exactly,' Mr. Wright said with a smile. 'Halloween was originally an old Celtic holiday called Samhain, which meant 'end of summer.' For the Celts it was the beginning of the new year, and it was the night when the veil between the worlds was thinnest.'

'What worlds?' Ted asked.

'The world of the living and the world of the dead. According to the Celts, on Halloween the invisible barriers between the worlds are lifted and the souls of the dead roam the earth. That's why we still dress up as ghosts and skeletons.'

'Gross,' said Cindy Cardell.

McKenzie didn't find it gross. She found it

terrifying. What if Halloween really was the night when the dead returned? Vanessa Grant seemed to have made it back before the holiday. But if there was any truth to the old beliefs – if this was a night when the normal barriers between the worlds dissolved – then the spirit that possessed Lilicat would soon be at her strongest.

'It wasn't only the dead,' Mr. Wright went on. 'Halloween loosed all sorts of magic – witches, fairies, goblins – everything that normally belongs to the unseen.'

The words made McKenzie even more uneasy. Where was Lilicat now? She sat quietly, concentrating on her friend, but she couldn't feel anything except the fear that had been with her all day.

At three o'clock sharp McKenzie tore out of school. Luckily, her parents had let her take the Toyota. Ten minutes later she was ringing the Caines' doorbell. Mrs. Caine answered the door, looking haggard.

'No sign of Lilicat?'

'No, and I've tried every place and every one I could think of. Do you have any ideas, Mack?'

'I don't know where she is,' McKenzie

answered honestly. 'But if I could go up to her room, I might be able to figure it out.'

Mrs. Caine didn't know about McKenzie's special ability, and McKenzie wasn't going to try to explain it. But what she hoped was that by being in Lilicat's room and concentrating hard enough, she'd be able to pick up some sort of vibration that would tell her where her friend was.

Upstairs, McKenzie looked around the familiar bedroom where she and Lilicat had had so many good times. An overwhelming sense of grief washed over her – almost as if Lilicat were dead.

No, McKenzie told herself. She's alive and I'm going to find her. She took off her jacket, sat down cross-legged on the floor, and closed her eyes. She had to concentrate now. To make herself see Lilicat – wherever she was.

She pictured Lilicat's shining black hair, the way the corners of her eyes crinkled when she was laughing – but the image quickly vanished. Instead she saw Vanessa Grant, wild hair flying. 'She's mine now,' Vanessa told her. 'She's all mine.'

McKenzie shuddered and stood up. Great, she thought bitterly. I've got this amazing ability that does nothing but scare the daylights out of me. What good is it if I've got no control over it? If I can't use it to stop the things it warns me about?

Maybe she ought to try something different. She went over to the dresser. Her eyes lit on the piggy bank, and she felt herself flinch. It reminded her of the day they'd met Vanessa Grant. The day this whole nightmare started. Still, it might be worth trying.

She picked up the little bank. 'All right, pig,' McKenzie said. 'I don't understand it, but Lilicat is crazy about you. Maybe you've got some vibrations that will help me reach her.'

Feeling a little silly, McKenzie stood in the center of the room, holding the pig. Lilicat, she thought, can you hear me? Lilicat, where are you? Can you feel me calling you?

This time there was nothing at all. McKenzie wondered briefly if she should have spoken to the pig in French.

Desperately she put the pig down and began searching the room again. She flipped through Lilicat's makeup, books, and tapes and finally opened the closet door. The denim jacket hung in the very center of the closet, and the second McKenzie saw it she started to tremble. She took it gingerly from the hanger.

Taking a deep breath, she put on the jacket

and was hit by a rush of evil so pure she nearly fell to the floor. She stumbled against the dresser, trying to keep her balance. What was it about the denim jacket that was doing this to her?

And then she realized. Vanessa Grant had worn it. It was not only connected to Lilicat, it was connected to Vanessa. And if she wanted to find Lilicat, she'd have to focus on Vanessa.

McKenzie felt the evil surround her like a thick, black mist. Like something she'd never find her way through. She wanted to rip off the jacket and run as far as she could. And yet she knew she could only help Lilicat if she rode out over this wave of fear, if she trusted in her own powers. Still cloaked in the jacket, she closed her eyes.

The man lies on the floor, the ends of his long, fair hair darkening with blood. The blood wells up from his back, down his arm, pooling on the wooden floor. The woman watches, a smile of contentment on her face. It is Lilicat's face. She sweeps her skirt back as the blood spreads toward the toe of her boot.

The man groans. Slowly, he pulls himself to his knees. Choking on his own blood, he gets out one broken word, 'Why?'

'You betrayed me.' Her voice is cool. 'You told me that if I would only stop traveling with the theater, you'd be with me. You asked me to wait here for you. Every night I prayed you'd return. And all the while you were with another.'

'No – ' he protests.

Her back to him, she continues. 'Tonight you appear at the door, as if you'd never left. You think your kisses make it all right. You expect me to welcome you. Well, you got the welcome you deserve.'

'I – never – '

She turns on him, furious. 'You'll never betray me again, I swear it. Never.'

He gets to his feet. He stumbles toward her. Eyes wide, she backs away. She raises the knife again. This time she will end it. There is a clattering sound. Then a hiss and a blaze of orange behind her. The woman turns. The wrought-iron candleholder lies flat on the floor. A line of flame licks across the wooden floor and along the edge of her satin skirt. The woman screams. It is too late. The flames rise. The heat is unbearable. Black smoke fills the room. The quilt and mattress catch fire. The mahogany dresser begins to smolder. The smell of burning flesh and hair fills the air. Then everything is caught in a curtain of blazing orange fire. He thought he'd leave me, the woman thinks. Now he never will. It's her last thought.

The man falls for the last time, his eyes wide with terror. He knows he will never get up again. Smoke fills his lungs. The flames are only inches from his body. In the light of the fire his face is clear. There's no mistaking it. It's Aidan.

CHAPTER 15

'No!' McKenzie breathed as the last traces of the vision faded. So Vanessa Grant was not only going to kill Lilicat; she was going to take Aidan with her. And McKenzie still had no idea of where to find her friend.

'Oh no,' moaned McKenzie, 'what if I don't get there in time?'

She started to pull off the denim jacket, wanting to rid herself of Vanessa's presence. Then she realized she couldn't. It was the jacket that would lead her to Vanessa. Suppressing a shudder, she pulled her own jacket over Lilicat's and forced herself to walk down the stairs at close to normal pace. The last thing she wanted was to alarm Lilicat's mother.

Mrs. Caine was waiting for her at the bottom of the staircase. 'Well?'

'I didn't figure out anything definite,' McKenzie admitted. 'But I'm going to keep looking for her. I'll let you know as soon as I find out anything.'

She hugged Mrs. Caine, and then she was out the door, running toward the car.

Don't let this have happened already, she prayed. Don't let me be too late.

She drove straight to Aidan's house, reminding herself he'd been in school that day, acting perfectly normal. There wasn't anything she could do about Lilicat right now, but maybe she could at least warn Aidan in time. His car wasn't in its usual place in front of the house, but his mother's station wagon was parked in the driveway.

McKenzie rang the doorbell and stood waiting. Someone had to be home – even if it was one of Aidan's mostly unhelpful brothers.

Mrs. Collins opened the door. 'Hello, McKenzie.' She sounded surprised.

'Hi, Mrs. C. Is Aidan here?'

'I'm afraid not.'

'Do you know where he is?'

Mrs. Collins ran a hand through her sandy hair. It was the same gesture Aidan used when he was tired. 'I just got in myself about ten minutes ago,' she told McKenzie. 'No one in this family ever seems to remember to leave a note when they're going somewhere.'

McKenzie smiled in spite of herself. Mrs. Collins taught English at the junior high, and all of her sons went to great lengths to avoid writing. Aidan would probably rather leave a drawing than a note. And he couldn't draw.

Something caught McKenzie's eye – a red light flashing on the table in the hall. It was the answering machine. McKenzie dismissed it and then looked again. Some instinct was urging her to pay attention to it.

'Mrs. Collins,' she said quickly, 'I know this sounds strange, but would it be possible for me to listen to the messages on your machine?'

Aidan's mother looked at her as if she were crazy.

'I really need to talk to Aidan. Maybe he called in and left a message saying where he is.'

Mrs. Collins smiled ruefully. 'That's not his style, but go ahead.'

McKenzie went over to the machine and pressed the playback button.

'Mrs. Collins, this is D & L Washing Machines. I'm sorry but our repairman has to cancel – '

'Not again!' Mrs. Collins groaned.

McKenzie forwarded to the next message. 'Hey, slimeball. You left your turtle at my house . . .' That was undoubtedly for Aidan's nine-year-old brother Rory, who had the unfortunate habit of leaving his pet turtle at other people's houses. McKenzie vividly remembered the time it had wound up in the Golds' fruit bowl.

She sped through a message for Aidan's father and another for his mom, and then found the one she'd been waiting for.

'Hi, Aidan, it's Lilicat. I went to Croton to visit my aunt, and now I'm ready to leave but my car won't start. Can you believe it? Sorry to bug you, but I really need your help. I'll owe you forever if you'll just come pick me up. The address is 99 Jennings Way. Love you.'

Mrs. Collins's eyebrows shot up at Lilicat's closing words, but she didn't say anything.

McKenzie glanced at the digital readout on the machine. It showed that the last message, Lilicat's message, had come in on October 31 at four o'clock. She checked her watch. Lilicat had called only about forty-five minutes ago. Did Aidan get the message? Was he on his way to Croton now?

'Well,' Mrs. Collins said sympathetically, 'I guess that explains it.'

No, it doesn't, McKenzie thought. Lilicat doesn't have an aunt in Croton.

CHAPTER 16

Croton. McKenzie got into her car, flipped open the glove compartment, and took out a map. The town was east of Lakeville, about twenty minutes away. She found Jennings Way and groaned. Jennings was a fairly long road off Bergen, the town's main street. Ninety-nine could be anywhere, and it was getting dark. 'Please,' McKenzie prayed, 'let me get there in time.'

She drove pushing the speed limit, hoping she wouldn't be stopped. She made good time until she reached the outskirts of Croton. She turned onto Broadway, the street that led into Bergen. Traffic was at a dead standstill. What is this, McKenzie wondered, an accident? She flipped on the radio, hoping for a traffic report. She got a blast of heavy metal.

In the distance a red light turned green, and the traffic inched forward. I can't believe this, McKenzie thought. She looked at the map again. There was no way onto Jennings except by Bergen Street. She was stuck. And while she waited, Lilicat and Aidan were playing out a deadly scene scripted by Vanessa Grant.

McKenzie heard a drum boom in the distance and suddenly realized what the problem was. 'Oh no,' she moaned, resting her forehead on the steering wheel. It was Halloween, and Croton was having its annual Halloween parade. The town of Croton wasn't known for much *except* its Halloween parade. Hundreds of people came from all over. The parade began just before sunset and went on for hours.

McKenzie studied the map again. She realized that there *were* a few other ways of getting onto Bergen. She turned left at the next corner. She found the street barricaded. Swearing at the parade, Croton, and Halloween in general, she turned round and tried another route. The drum-beat grew louder and the crowd began to build. Ghouls, ghosts, and demons filled the streets. McKenzie slowed as a ring of teenagers dressed as skeletons surrounded her car. 'Trick or treat!' they shouted, pounding on the windows.

She pressed hard on her horn. Two boys

jumped up onto the hood, another onto the trunk, and a fourth onto the roof. Another smashed his face against her window; his mask of bones was grotesque. McKenzie fought back tears of frustration and fear. They weren't going to let her go.

The Toyota shook. What if the boys turned it over? What if they broke in through the windows? Two more skeletons joined the others, flattening themselves against her windshield. 'Come on out, little girl,' they taunted. 'You belong to us tonight!'

Slowly, McKenzie inched the car forward. She didn't want to hurt anyone, but she wasn't about to become their captive. Not when Aidan and Lilicat's lives depended on her.

The boys sprang from the car as the beginning of the parade approached. McKenzie felt a rush of relief. A second later she froze as she got a clear glimpse of the beginning of the procession. The scene before her was straight out of a nightmare. Huge witches, at least seven feet tall, came loping toward her. After a moment she realized that they were on stilts. The seven of them wore long gray robes covering the stilts, hideous masks, and long, stringy wigs. Moving in time to the heavy beat of the drum, they used giant-size brooms to sweep the street in front of them. Why was it such an eerie sight? She thought of what Mr. Wright had said. It was as if they were sweeping away everything normal and sane that belonged to the everyday world. It was as if they were preparing the way for a night of magic and terror.

Swallowing hard, McKenzie turned the car around. She could feel herself shaking with frustration and anger. She was just so rattled by this crazy night. I've got to get out of the car, she told herself. The only way I'll ever reach Jennings is on foot.

Maneuvering back onto a side street, she parked the car at the curbside. She got out, pushing her way through the crowds. She glanced at her watch. It was after six. The sun was gone. What if she didn't reach Lilicat and Aidan in time? What if they were already . . . no, she wouldn't even let herself think that.

'Hey, where's your costume?' demanded a vampire at her shoulder.

McKenzie didn't even bother to answer. She pushed past him angrily. Finally reaching Bergen Street, she wound her way through the parade, ducking as she collided with a giant rabbit. This is beyond weird, she thought. The rabbit offered her a carrot, and McKenzie ran.

She saw the corner of Jennings and turned

146

onto it. She stood for a moment, her breath coming in gasps. Ninety-nine, she thought, scanning the house numbers. She was about to start her search when an arm reached out and grabbed her around the waist.

McKenzie felt the air go out of her and tiny red spots danced before her eyes. She wrenched herself around, unable to break the grip that held her. And she saw that whoever – or whatever – had her in its grasp was holding a long silver knife.

CHAPTER 17

With a wild burst of energy McKenzie broke out of her attacker's grip. Turning around, she raised her fists, ready to fight for her life. All of the self-defense moves she'd learned had fled from her mind.

'Trick or treat!' yelled the kid who had grabbed her.

McKenzie felt the panic drain out of her, replaced by a numb sense of disbelief. The kid was wearing a scarred, disfigured mask. The knife in his hand was made of rubber.

'What's with you?' he asked, genuinely puzzled. 'It's Halloween. Remember?'

McKenzie nodded, and he vanished back into the crowd. Still feeling jittery, she began to scan the house numbers. She was standing in front of number twelve. Ninety-nine was probably at the very end of the street.

Once again McKenzie began to run, and fast. Her feet pounded against the pavement. The shadows of the trees that lined the street whipped past her on either side. She was pushing her body to its limit.

She didn't need the street number to recognize 99 Jennings Way. She had only seen glimpses of it in her vision. But that had been enough to leave a vivid impression. Besides, she could feel the evil rising from the ramshackle house that stood before her.

The house had been abandoned long ago. If the gray wood siding had ever been painted, there was no trace of it now. The windows were boarded up, two of the front steps were missing altogether, and from the way the boards on the side of the house were blackened, it looked as if there'd once been a fire. The oak tree that had once stood at the side of the house was now a sawed-off stump.

McKenzie wanted to race straight into the house and rescue her friends. But she couldn't run anymore. The scary sight of the house had stopped her cold. She stumbled through the overgrown front yard. There were still a few rays of sunlight left, and a full moon was rising in the sky. But the house seemed to suck in all the light. It was darker than anything else on the street, and McKenzie had a sudden crazy fear that the house would suck her in too. That once she stepped through the doorway, she'd never get out.

She jumped as the porch's rotting banister snapped beneath her hand. I don't want to touch this place anyway, McKenzie thought. She forced herself to continue up the stairs. The front door had been wedged open, possibly by Aidan. Her sense of evil grew more intense. It was what she'd felt in her dreams, what had nearly knocked her to the floor when she'd put on the jacket. She still had the jacket on. Like a magnet, it was pulling her toward what was inside. Whatever it was, the evil was in this house. She couldn't quite believe she had to go inside.

Carefully, McKenzie crossed the porch. In a flash she remembered the vision of the woman and the man embracing there. They had stood there once, how many years ago? Had they been there tonight, somehow living again through Lilicat and Aidan?

She lingered for a moment beside the open door. What if she never came out of this? She pushed the thought aside and tried to think of Lilicat – Lilicat teasing her about something and laughing. McKenzie knew that if she didn't go inside, she'd never see Lilicat again.

She stepped over the threshold. It took a moment for her eyes to adjust to the darkness. She stood quietly. Evil surrounded her now. She could feel it. She had had time to catch her breath. But somehow she couldn't. Not here.

Wishing she had a flashlight, she began to search the first floor. The house was a shambles. Entire sections of the floor were missing. McKenzie walked through the living room. The wallpaper was stained and faded. Pieces of a plaid sofa were strewn about the rooms, as if the sofa had been ravaged by a giant animal. Empty bottles and cans and bits of clothing littered the floors. A bulky console TV, whose screen had been kicked in, sat in the middle of the room. Everything smelled of smoke and decay.

McKenzie walked into the kitchen. Roaches, startled by her footsteps, darted across the floor. There was a broken table that looked like it had been chopped up for firewood. There was a hole in the wall where the oven used to be. The doors on the cupboard had been torn off. A small refrigerator stood with the door hanging open. McKenzie felt her stomach heave. Something inside was rotting. Except for a narrow counter covered with filth, there was nothing else in the kitchen.

Covering her mouth with her sleeve, McKenzie made her way out of the kitchen and into the alcove. She stood beneath the arch, peering into the shadows. She saw no one on the ground floor. It didn't surprise her. She knew where she had to go.

Slowly, McKenzie climbed the stairway. She gasped. The wooden banister had given her a splinter.

She crossed the landing and peered into what were once bedrooms. On the floor of one lay a scorched mattress. Another room held pieces of wood so badly broken that McKenzie wasn't even sure they'd ever been furniture. Light glimmered in the third room – a shattered mirror.

McKenzie checked the last room. Ripped, faded curtains hung from the windows. The room was empty.

Reluctantly, she returned to the stairs and climbed the last flight. The door at the top was made of four rough boards and was fastened with a crossbar. The attic. A wave of nausea went through her and she began to shiver violently. There was no question in her mind.

The attic was where she would find Lilicat and Aidan.

McKenzie pushed open the attic door. A faint reddish ray of light came through a broken window. The light fell across the filthy wooden floor. Spiders scuttled away from her, hiding beneath stacks of yellowed newspapers. There was nothing else in the attic, just piles of cardboard boxes and papers, smelling of mold.

At the far end of the attic the stub of a candle burned. McKenzie shuddered. The attic was freezing, but even if it had been heated, what she saw before her would have chilled her to the bone.

'Lilicat!' she said, but no sound came out. Her voice was gone, paralyzed by terror.

Lilicat stood beneath the eaves, dressed in the gypsy clothing, her face hidden beneath the heavy makeup. Her hair, always so straight and sleek, hung around her shoulders in dark, wild curls.

Aidan stood across from her, wearing jeans, a white shirt, and a black vest.

'I waited for you,' Lilicat was saying. She held out one hand. Her bracelets slid against each other with a light, familiar clink. 'I've waited for you for two long years.'

Aidan stared at her in confusion. 'Lilicat, what's with you? What are you talking about?'

She stepped up to him. Beneath her skirt, McKenzie saw black lace-up boots. 'No!' she screamed. Again, no sound came out. The evil was working. It was freezing everything. It had trapped her as completely as it had trapped her friends.

Lilicat reached up and ran one hand along Aidan's cheek, caressing him.

Startled, he stepped back. But she reached for him with that hand and sank her fingers into his arm, holding on as if she'd never let go. Slowly she brought her other hand out from behind her back. And in it she held a gleaming silver knife.

CHAPTER 18

Aidan saw the knife and struggled to free himself from Lilicat's grasp.

'You,' Lilicat said in a voice that wasn't her own. It was Vanessa Grant's voice, and it was filled with venom. 'You betray me, and now you think you can just come running back.'

'Lilicat!' Aidan sounded angry, but also frightened.

'Lilicat? Is that her name? I see you don't even remember mine! You keep me waiting here, and all the time you're with another. You think you can betray me and then come back as if nothing had happened.' Vanessa's voice rose in fury as Lilicat raised the long silver knife high above her head. 'Did you think that maybe if you left me here long enough I'd die? Don't you know I'm going to take you with me?'

McKenzie was trembling, sweating. She knew what would happen next. And that gave her the strength to break the spell. She hurled herself across the room, colliding with Lilicat. She grabbed Lilicat's wrist, the one that held the knife.

But she was too late. Struggling against McKenzie, Lilicat wrenched away and plunged the blade deep into Aidan's shoulder.

He cried out in pain and fell to his knees, a dark stain welling out along his shirt. Blood was running down his arm, soaking the white shirt and black vest. It stained his hands and wrists deep red.

Above him, Lilicat stood smiling. She raised the bloody knife in her right hand. She was going to finish the job.

'No!' McKenzie screamed. 'You'll kill him!' She tackled Lilicat, knocking her down. The two girls rolled across the floor, wrestling. McKenzie kept one hand on Lilicat's right arm, holding the knife away. Furious, Lilicat slashed the air.

McKenzie grabbed for Lilicat's wrist and slammed it hard against the floor, knocking the knife free. It clattered along the wood boards.

'Give it back!' Vanessa's voice screamed.

Frantically, Lilicat struggled beneath

McKenzie, reaching for the blade. Behind her McKenzie heard Aidan moan. At least he was still alive.

Lilicat seemed more than alive. She was fighting like a wild thing, pulling McKenzie's hair, trying to scratch her eyes out.

McKenzie ducked backward as Lilicat tried to smash her in the face with her elbow. But Lilicat still caught her on the chin. McKenzie felt the impact straight up to her eye. The whole side of her face throbbed.

Now Lilicat's fingernails were digging into her, ripping deep furrows across her face. 'Lilicat!' McKenzie screamed.

Enraged, Lilicat reached for the other side of her face.

Using the last of her strength, McKenzie managed to pin her. There was the knife. McKenzie might be able to reach it. And then what? Who was she fighting here? Lilicat or Vanessa Grant? Was there anything left of her friend?

'Nooooooo!' Lilicat wailed.

The cry startled McKenzie. Was she hurting Lilicat? And then she saw why her friend was screaming. During their fight a corner of the green satin skirt had touched the candle.

The smell of burning cloth filled the air. A

small yellow flame rippled along the fabric. The flame rushed toward Lilicat. McKenzie rolled on top of her again, trying to smother the flame. But she wasn't fast enough. Flames crackled as one of the cartons began to blaze, and a line of fire streaked across the wood floor. It caught the hem of the green satin skirt again. Lilicat was burning.

'Help me!' Lilicat screamed. 'Please, help me!'

CHAPTER 19

The fire that McKenzie had seen and dreamed was real. It was burning the gypsy's skirt, and it would take them all with it.

'Help!' Lilicat kept screaming. Wide-eyed with terror, she tried to roll away from her own skirt, but she couldn't. The stink of burning material filled the small room. 'Help me!' But at the same time, she kept fighting McKenzie, kicking and struggling.

A hiss caught McKenzie's attention. She looked behind her. A pile of newspapers had burst into flame. Black smoke began to billow toward them. Behind them on the floor lay Aidan; he wasn't moving.

Desperate, McKenzie reached for Lilicat's waist and ripped the skirt off. She didn't stop there. She tore away the shawl. She ripped off her blouse.

Lilicat, wearing only a camisole and slip, stopped struggling. 'Mack?' she asked. Her eyes stared at McKenzie in confusion. And then they closed.

'Lilicat?' McKenzie was frantic. Had she gotten her friend back only to lose her? 'Lilicat, you've got to get up!' Then she turned toward her boyfriend. 'Aidan!' she screamed. 'Help me!' He groaned but began to move. He tried to raise himself off the floor.

Flames licked across the floor and toward the window. The heat was becoming unbearable. Everything was illuminated in the eerie orange light of the flames.

Aidan had managed to get to his feet. He stumbled toward them. One hand clutched his bloody shoulder, and he was choking on the smoke. 'We've got to get out of here,' he gasped. Kneeling beside Lilicat, he used one arm to help her to her feet.

Coughing violently, McKenzie pulled off the denim jacket and held it over her mouth and nose. Lilicat stood with one arm around Aidan and one around McKenzie. Her eyes were open now, but she was clearly in shock. It seemed that the three of them were standing on the only patch of floor that wasn't on fire.

McKenzie jumped at a crackling sound to their right. Another pile of cartons went up. The flames reached for the ceiling. The beams started to catch. Small tongues of fire licked across the boards. The ceiling wouldn't last long. It was going to come down on them.

'Come on!' Aidan was moving toward the door.

'No!' Lilicat cried.

They would have to go through the fire to reach the door. McKenzie forced herself to move forward.

Terrified, Lilicat pulled back.

Aidan looked at McKenzie, then toward the door. She saw that he was as scared as she was, and seriously hurt. And yet they would have to cross the flames and pull Lilicat with them.

McKenzie smelled the stink of hair burning. She screamed as she saw the ends of her own auburn hair curl into tight black springs, singed by the fire. The heat was all around her. She felt it blazing against her hands and wrists and face. She could barely breathe. How long before her skin blistered? How long before she was burned alive?

There was an earsplitting explosion as the

tiny attic window shattered. Air rushed into the room, sending the flames soaring.

McKenzie couldn't move. Her vision was coming true, all of it. She was paralyzed with terror. This time there wasn't anything she could do to change things. Her special senses hadn't done her any good at all. She'd not only seen Lilicat's and Aidan's death. She'd foreseen her own.

CHAPTER 20

A hard jerk on McKenzie's arm snapped her out of shock. 'Come on!' Aidan choked out the words. 'Help me pull her out of here!'

McKenzie nodded. The smoke stung her eyes and throat. She could feel her eyes tearing, her nose running.

'Now!' Aidan yelled.

McKenzie couldn't even see the door ahead of them. It was all yellow-orange flame and black smoke. It was their only chance.

Holding the jacket in front of her face, she forced herself forward, pulling Lilicat along with her. She felt the flames around her ankles. They scorched her sneakers. They danced around her jeans. Thick clouds of black smoke billowed up. She couldn't see. She held on to Lilicat and ran.

Then suddenly they were through the door and on the staircase. She was still caught in a thick black web of smoke, but she could feel cooler air below. She grabbed for the banister and drew her hand back at once. The banister was white hot and smoldering. It seared an angry red mark across her palm.

Aidan started down the stairs, his good hand still steadying Lilicat. Lilicat moved like someone in a trance. McKenzie followed, jumping as she heard what had to be part of the roof caving in. Oh, please let us make it out alive, she prayed. Please let us make it out alive.

She heard the flames behind her. Heard a rush of air and a crackling. Heard the staircase catch fire. She didn't let herself look back.

McKenzie couldn't believe they actually made it down the three flights of stairs. The fire raced through the old wood house as if it were paper. Thick black smoke was everywhere. Behind them the heat was so intense McKenzie couldn't believe they were still moving, still alive.

At last they burst through the front door. They were outside. The three of them collapsed on the overgrown lawn, coughing and choking. McKenzie took in deep gulps of the cool night air. Sirens echoed through the night, and she realized that someone had reported the fire. It was too late for the house, she knew, but not too late for them.

McKenzie and Lilicat sat in orange vinyl chairs outside Croton Hospital's emergency room. Lilicat had been released first, after being treated for smoke inhalation and minor burns. McKenzie had also been treated for smoke inhalation and first-degree burns. Her throat still felt as if it had been scraped raw. The doctors had dressed the scratches on her face and bandaged her blistered hand. She'd lost two inches of hair on her right side. She'd have to get it evened out, but that was the least of her worries. Now they waited together for Aidan, and their parents, whom the hospital had insisted on calling.

At last she saw Aidan. He was in a wheelchair, being wheeled toward them by an orderly. He, too, was missing a shock of hair, and his face looked very gray. McKenzie gulped. She hadn't wanted to believe that the knife wound was serious. After all, he'd gotten himself out of the burning house. But seeing him there in the wheelchair . . .

The orderly stopped the chair in front of her, gave Aidan a weary glance, and said, 'He's lost some blood, but we're gonna let him go home tonight.'

Aidan got to his feet a little unsteadily.

'Aidan!' McKenzie threw her arms around him.

'Oww!' He winced and drew back. 'Careful with that shoulder.'

'Sorry.' McKenzie stepped back at once, then touched it gently. 'You've got a mountain of bandages under there.'

'No kidding. They said I was lucky. It was just a flesh wound. No muscle or blood vessels severed.' He ran his other hand through her smoke-blackened hair. 'You don't look so good yourself? Are you all right?'

She nodded, blinking back tears. Why was she crying now? Everything was fine.

Aidan put his good arm around her and drew her to his side.

'Mack?' Lilicat had barely spoken since they escaped the house. Now she sat huddled in Aidan's coat, looking very small. 'What happened back there?'

'What do you remember?' McKenzie asked.

Lilicat shook her head. 'Not much. I remember cutting school this morning. . . . Oh, God, my mother's going to kill me.'

'She'll be glad to see you,' McKenzie assured her. 'She's been worried sick.'

'I don't remember the rest of the morning,' Lilicat went on. 'But sometime after lunch I got this urge to hitch to Croton.'

'You hitched?' Aidan said. 'Your mother *will* kill you.'

Lilicat still looked a little dazed. 'I think I made a phone call.'

'You did,' McKenzie and Aidan said together.

'Then the next thing I remember is seeing that house and going inside.'

'And then?' McKenzie prompted.

'Nothing. Until we were all back out on the lawn choking to death.'

'Whew!' Aidan said. 'You're definitely missing a few pieces, but I am too. What was all that stuff about me betraying you?'

Lilicat looked completely blank.

'That wasn't Lilicat,' McKenzie explained. 'That was Vanessa Grant.'

'Well, that explains everything,' Aidan joked.

'It gets weirder,' said McKenzie. 'From what I can tell, Vanessa Grant lived a long time ago. She worked in the theater as a wardrobe mistress. She was in love with a man who looked a lot like you, Aidan. She must have been traveling with the theater, going to other parts of the country on tour or something, because her lover asked her to wait for him. So she gave up her own job and took one as a servant in that house. She waited for him for two years. And he betrayed her somehow – became involved with another woman, I think – and then came back to her. He expected that she would just take him back. I'm not sure about this part, but she may have been sick or something. She thought he was going to leave her to die – and she was right.'

'This is creepy,' Lilicat said.

'Not as creepy as what comes next. I think Vanessa Grant died in a fire. But something in her – her spirit or ghost or whatever – never did. She had to avenge herself. She was determined to take him with her. And so she keeps going back. People *think* they've seen her recently. But she actually died many years ago. From what I can figure out, each time she uses the clothing to possess a young woman. And she looks for a young man who reminds her of her lover.'

'Do you mean she keeps coming back to life?' Aidan asked.

'Not exactly,' McKenzie said. 'I mean, we saw her at the flea market, and so did the man who sold the antique jewelry. And Gillian saw her in Lilicat's room. But after that she only appeared in my visions and dreams. She's not *real*. She needed someone who was really alive – like Lilicat – to work her revenge. So she possessed her through the gypsy clothes.' McKenzie's eyes met Aidan's. 'And then she found Aidan, so she could force him to die with her.'

'Nice lady,' said Aidan with a shudder.

'You mean I almost killed Aidan?' Lilicat's voice was shaking.

Aidan's gray eyes were filled with disbelief. 'You really don't remember stabbing me? Or nearly tearing Mack apart when she tried to take the knife from you?'

Lilicat shook her head, her bottom lip trembling. 'I'm sorry.' Her body was racked with sobs. 'I'm so sorry . . .'

'It's all right, Lilicat,' McKenzie said, holding her. 'It was never you. It was Vanessa Grant and she's gone now. We've got you back, and that's all that matters.'

EPILOGUE

A golden autumn morning in Bakersfield. A warm Indian summer wind blows through an open field littered with dried cornstalks. The trees are bright with red, yellow, and orange leaves. Piles of pumpkins fill the air with an earthy smell.

The Wickham flea market is setting up. Vans and cars are pulling in. Tables are being unfolded. Boxes and cartons are being unpacked.

An older man with steady dark eyes opens large, rectangular wooden cases lined with velvet. Antique necklaces and rings sparkle in the morning sun. He picks up a Victorian brooch, quartz set in silver, holds it up to the light, and watches the rainbows play along the table.

A young man arranges a collection of mechanical banks and old toys. Beside him a woman begins to unwrap handblown glass hurricane lamps. Across the way, another man fills a clothing rack with old silk kimonos.

More cars and trucks pull in. More stalls are set up. The morning sun warms the field, and the hum of insects grows louder. Someone sets out a fresh urn of coffee, and the dealers all gather and exchange news. Bees hover near an open box of doughnuts. The stiff breeze takes a stack of Styrofoam cups and sends it rolling through the grass.

A young man with long hair sets up a table filled with old stringed instruments – guitars and fiddles, banjos and lutes. He perches on a stool above his wares, a guitar on his knee, and begins to pick out the strains of an old ballad.

No one notices the gypsy clothes that magically appear on one of the racks, or the wild-haired woman who sells them. . . .

Turn the page
for a chilling preview of

The Witness
(Book #2 of *The Power*) . . .

It's ten o'clock. The house is quiet. A tall teenage girl climbs the stairs. A long black braid hangs down her back. She checks on the children. They are all asleep.

The girl goes back down the stairs. She sits on the sofa and stares at the television. The doorbell rings.

The girl glances toward the door. She stands up, goes to the door, and peers through the window. She sees a man standing in the yellow porch light. He is wearing a blue uniform. He thrusts a badge toward the window.

The police!

The girl unlocks the door. She opens it. The man's cap is pulled low over his eyes. She can't see his face.

He says something to her. What is it? She

nods. Her eyes dart around. Is everything all right?

She lets him in. She closes the door.

She walks through the living room. He follows her. Her long black braid swings back and forth. Back and forth.

They walk through the kitchen. There's another door. The girl opens the door – it's dark in there. Is it a closet? No. Too dark.

The girl flicks a switch. A dim light goes on. There's a stairway. It leads to the basement. But now the man flicks the switch. The light goes off. It's dark.

The girl's eyes widen. She turns to face him. Her mouth is open. She's going to scream!

She can't scream. He claps his hand over her mouth. He pushes her. It's dark. She stumbles down the stairs. She can't see.

He grabs her braid. He stuffs it into her mouth. She can't make a sound. He's holding something. A knife.

She shakes her head. She squirms. His hand grips her neck. He grips tighter, tighter. She can't scream. There's hair in her mouth. He pushes her back. She falls to the floor. It's cold and damp. The knife flashes above her. The man's eyes are closed. The knife plunges down.

McKenzie Gold screamed out loud. She sat up, gasping for breath. Her hands clutched her face, then her chest. She turned on the light and checked her hands for blood. They were clean and dry. She wasn't hurt. But where was she?

She looked around the room – a modern living room, vaguely familiar. She was lying on a white sofa. A lamp was lit on the chrome-and-glass end table next to it. Her math textbook lay open on the coffee table. It wasn't home – not at all – but it was a place she knew fairly well. . . . A neighbor's house. The Donaldsons'. She was baby-sitting – yes, taking care of their son Jeffrey and daughter Jennifer. Everything was all right.

McKenzie leaned back against the plump white cushions, breathing more easily now. It was only a dream, she told herself. Only a dream.

But *was* it? Deep down, McKenzie knew that this was more than just a dream. Somewhere in a cold, damp basement lay a teenage girl with a long black braid. And that girl wasn't dreaming. She was dead.

McKenzie reached into her backpack for her tiny tape recorder. She had bought it to record interviews for the articles she wrote for her high school newspaper, the *Guardian*. But she used it for another, very different purpose, too. Sometimes McKenzie's dreams came true: she would see scenes of terror, mystery, or just some ordinary occurrence in her sleep and in the morning awake to find that there were not just dreams – what she had seen had actually taken place. At other times a vision would sweep over her consciousness like a wave, wiping out her physical surroundings and replacing them with a scene of something that was happening somewhere else, had happened in the past, or would happen in the future. These dreams and visions were very important to her; she wanted to remember every detail, for she knew they had some special meaning.

McKenzie pressed RECORD and began to speak haltingly into the tape recorder. 'It's Thursday night, pretty late, I think. I just had a terrible dream. I saw a girl, a baby-sitter, with a long black braid. She was wearing Levis, a white shirt, red socks, black high-top sneakers. . . . She was in a house, in the living room. . . . There was a red rug on the floor; a red, white and blue patchwork quilt on the wall behind the television. . . . The TV was big, new looking. . . . a Sony, I think. The walls were pale blue. . . . There was a painting – a reproduction – over the sofa. It showed some men in a boat, sailing. . . . The sofa was sort of modern, covered in white cotton, and there were two upholstered chairs, also white, on either side of it. . . . There were magazines on the coffee table – *Sports Illustrated, People, National Geographic.* . . . The doorbell rang. A man was at the door. He was dressed as a policeman, but I don't think he really was a policeman. The girl let him in. I followed her to the basement. I was staring at her braid. I just couldn't get that braid out of my mind. It was driving me crazy.'

McKenzie recorded everything she could remember. Every detail counts, she told herself. If this murder really happened, she could help the police catch the killer.

McKenzie felt better as she turned the tape recorder off. She heard a car pull into the driveway and ran to the window to see who it was. The Donaldsons were home.

She gathered her things and quickly neatened up the living room. Mr. and Mrs. Donaldson came in, smelling of smoke and perfume and smiling from their evening out.

'Thank you for staying so late, McKenzie,' said Mrs. Donaldson. 'I know it's a strain on a school night.' Sarah Donaldson was an attractive woman in her mid-thirties. She reminded McKenzie of the glamorous career women she saw in old movies. 'But we had such a wonderful time. We'll pay you extra for staying after midnight.' She reached into her purse and pulled out some bills, which she gave to McKenzie. 'Thanks again, dear. Was everything all right?'

McKenzie smiled nervously. The nightmare still lingered in her mind, still felt real to her. But it *wasn't* real, she reminded herself again. She wanted desperately to believe that.

'Everything was fine,' she assured the Donaldsons with only a slight tremor in her voice. 'Jeffrey and Jennifer and I watched *The Little Mermaid*, and then they went to bed at nine. Jeffrey even brushed his teeth without any argument. Everything was absolutely fine.'

'Glad to hear it,' said Mr. Donaldson. He was a big man with an affable smile. 'I'll walk you home.'

'Oh, don't worry about me, Mr. Donaldson. It's only down the street. I'll be all right.'

'Nonsense,' said Mrs. Donaldson. 'It's one o'clock in the morning. You hear such terrible things these days. Have you been following the story of that man who's running around killing young girls in Naugatuck? It's terrifying!' She shuddered and added, 'George will walk you home, McKenzie. I insist.'

'Thanks.' Actually, McKenzie was relieved to

have an escort, even though her house was only three doors away.

The night was dark and moonless. McKenzie was glad to see that her father had remembered to leave the porch light on and the hall light inside, too. In fact, just the sight of her cozy blue Victorian house, with its white gingerbread trim and big wraparound porch, made McKenzie feel better.

Mr. Donaldson walked her up to the door and waited until she was safely inside. Then he waved and walked back home.

McKenzie's parents had already gone to bed, so she went straight to her room. She quickly changed into the big red T-shirt she wore instead of pajamas. She stepped into the bathroom to brush her teeth, then climbed into bed and turned off the light.

Everything was so quiet. The whole neighborhood was asleep. But when McKenzie listened more closely, she could hear the refrigerator humming. Then a creak. What was that? . . . A footstep on the stairs?

She sat up and turned on the light. She listened again. It was just one of the little noises the old house always made. Still, McKenzie didn't feel much like sleeping. She was afraid she'd have that awful nightmare again.

She tossed and turned all night, never more than half asleep. Every time she closed her eyes, the dream threatened to return. He heart pounded, and her mind grew numb with fear. Could her dream have already come true? It wouldn't be the first time. But nothing she had dreamed before had ever been this terrible.

McKenzie felt herself drifting down toward sleep again. . . . A long black braid – the red rug – was it red? – the doorbell ringing – looks like a policeman – he is a policeman, isn't he? – no, he's a *killer*.

McKenzie sat up with a start, chilled. Her bedcovers had fallen off. She pulled them around her and leaned back against the headboard. It was almost morning. The sun was rising, and her room was beginning to glow. There were all her familiar things: her gauzy white curtains; the recessed window seat, piled with colorful cushions, where she liked to read; the lumpy, metal sculptures she had made in her father's studio, shaped like cats, birds, seal, and deer; her book-lined shelves; her favorite rag doll from when she was little. . . . McKenzie was coming back to earth now. There were no murderers here. Everything was going to be all right.

She checked her big red alarm clock: five

thirty. Normally she didn't get up until six thirty, but there was no point in going back to sleep now. She slipped out of bed, got dressed for school, and went downstairs.

In the kitchen, sitting by his food dish, was McKenzie's old black cat, Blue. Everyone else was still asleep.

'There you are,' McKenzie said, opening the refrigerator door. Blue ran to the fridge and stuck his head inside. 'Don't worry, I'll feed you,' McKenzie promised. She pulled an open can of cat food from the refrigerator, grabbed a spoon, and plopped the stuff into Blue's dish. He ate greedily.

It was still only six o'clock. I might as well make a nice breakfast for everybody, McKenzie thought. I haven't got anything else to do between now and seven.

She was mixing pancake batter when her mother appeared, still in her bathrobe. McKenzie looked very much like her mom – they were both tall, thin, freckled and auburn haired. Joanne McKenzie Gold wore her hair short and wavy, whereas McKenzie's was long and straight. The only other difference was in their eyes: Joanne's were sky blue, but McKenzie's were a stormy gray-green, just like her father's.

'Well,' said Mrs. Gold, giving her daughter a kiss. 'Isn't this a nice surprise. What inspired you to get up so early and go to all this trouble? You're not going to ask for your own car again, are you?'

McKenzie smiled. 'No, Mom. I just woke up early and thought I'd do something constructive with the time.'

Mrs. Gold reached for the coffeepot. 'Are you sure everything's all right?' she asked. She could usually sense when something was bothering McKenzie. 'You're not worried about that math test today, are you?'

'No more than usual,' McKenzie replied. 'I studied hard last night. I think I'm ready for it.'

'Good. I only wish I could say the same for Jimmy. He's supposed to know how to multiply by nine today. I tried to help him learn it, but he didn't seem very interested. He wanted to know why he couldn't just use a calculator.'

'Well, why can't I?' Jimmy said sleepily. McKenzie's eight-year-old brother shuffled into the kitchen. His curly brown hair was still tousled from sleep. 'McKenzie's making pancakes? Did she ask you for a car again, Mom?'

'Not yet,' said Mrs. Gold. She pulled a comb from her pocket and approached her son warily.

184

'Jimmy, just let me run this comb through your hair once, real quick – '

Jimmy ducked and cried out, 'Mom!'

'Come on, Jimmy. It'll only take a second.' She managed to corner him by the pantry. But before she could touch his unruly curls, he scrambled away again.

'Stop it, Mom!' Jimmy whined. 'I *like* it messy.'

'Honestly, you'd think I was torturing the poor child,' said Mrs. Gold. 'He's just like his father.'

McKenzie began flipping the pancakes from the griddle to a platter. 'The pancakes are ready,' she announced.

'I'll call your father,' said Mrs. Gold. 'Shelby! Breakfast!'

Shelby Gold appeared in the kitchen dressed for work in jeans and a plaid flannel shirt. He owned a hardware store in Lakeville. Actually, it was *the* hardware store in town. His grandfather had started it in 1906, and it had been in the family ever since.

'Good morning, good morning!' he said merrily. 'Good morning, Joanne,' he said, kissing his wife; 'good morning, Jimmy,' kissing his son; 'good morning, McKenzie, the queen of pancakes.' He kissed McKenzie and took her platter of pancakes to the table. 'How did you know I would wake up craving pancakes this morning, McKenzie? I dreamed about them all night long.'

McKenzie smiled and shrugged.

'The old mind-reader trick, eh?' Mr. Gold joked. The Golds were no longer surprised by their daughter's unusual psychic abilities. When she was very young, they had taken her to a psychologist to be tested after she started sleepwalking and having waking dreams. The psychologist had been stumped, but the Golds had learned to accept McKenzie's power – her knowing what they were going to say before they said it, dreaming vividly of events before they happened, and so on – as just one of the many ways their daughter was different from other people's children. As far as McKenzie's parents were concerned, she was prettier, smarter, more creative, more charming, and a better mind reader than other girls, and that was that.

'It's not much of a trick when it comes to you and pancakes, Dad,' said McKenzie. 'You always crave them!'

'Well, I still say it comes in handy sometimes. Pour the juice, Jimmy, my boy. We're about to have a feast.'

McKenzie blushed. Her father's enthusiasm embarrassed her and pleased her at the same time.

'How about a little music with our breakfast?' said Mr. Gold, pushing back his chair. He stood up and turned on the radio. A Chopin sonata filled the room.

McKenzie served the pancakes, taking just two for herself. She wasn't very hungry this morning – her dream was still haunting her. That knife; the cold, damp basement floor; the look in the girl's eyes . . .

The music ended and the news came on.

'This just in,' the announcer said. 'A young girl has been murdered in Barrington. Barrington police suspect that the killing may be connected to the recent series of murders in Naugatuck and are contacting Naugatuck police about the incident. We'll give you more details as they come in.'

McKenzie's fork clattered to the floor. Oh my God, she thought. I was right. It wasn't just a dream. It actually happened. I witnessed a real murder!